Oil City Library

Oil City, Pa.

Memorial Book
in memory of
Robert A. Jackson

presented by
Teny Petrelli, Florence Puleo,
and Jennie Schell

THE COMPLETE BOOK OF
PRACTICAL
HANDLOADING

THE COMPLETE BOOK OF
PRACTICAL
HANDLOADING

JOHN WOOTTERS

WINCHESTER PRESS

Copyright © 1976 by John Wootters. All rights reserved.
Library of Congress Catalog Card Number: 76-7925
ISBN: 0-87691-215-3

Library of Congress Cataloging in Publication Data
Wooters, John.
    The complete book of practical handloading.
    Includes index.
    1. Handloading of ammunition. I. Title.
TS538.3.W66   683'.406   76-7925
ISBN 0-87691-215-3

Published by Winchester Press
205 E. 42nd Street
New York, N.Y. 10017

Printed in the United States of America.

To
JEANNIE

Although coincidental, it's appropriate that this book
is published on our Silver Wedding Anniversary

Contents

Foreword

Handloading ammunition is as distinctively American as baseball. Although common in this nation since the invention of self-contained cartridges, reloading has only recently begun to be an important pastime for shooters elsewhere. Even now, only a tiny minority of gunners reload their own ammunition in Canada, Australia, South Africa, Great Britain, and a few of the western European nations.

One reason is that relatively few governments are comfortable with the knowledge that their citizens have free access to gunpowder, primers, and bullets and the tools and technology with which to assemble them into functional ammunition. Such freedom is of course unthinkable for the majority of the world's people, who may not even possess firearms.

Against that background, I'm proud that we Americans have the Second Amendment which guarantees that our right to keep and bear firearms shall not be infringed, and proud of the shooting heritage represented in that Article of our Bill of Rights. Since handloading is an integral part of that heritage, it can be regarded as one symbol of American liberty, and that is one of the reasons I've labored and brought forth this book. As it is written, the forces which would deprive us of our right to own and lawfully use guns are gathering strength for a fresh assault upon that right, via the public media, in the schools, and on Capitol Hill. Perhaps the writing of this book is a gesture of defiance to that movement; I'd prefer to believe that it is an affirmation of my faith that it will fail once more, and that Americans will forever enjoy the shooting sports, including handloading, as they have in the past.

I've been reloading my ammo for all purposes for so long that it's difficult to remember all those who helped me get started, and thus helped me write *A Complete Guide to Practical Handloading*. Two of them were my mother and father, who encouraged my interests in shooting, firearms, and hunting almost from birth. Others, whom I never had the pleasure of knowing personally, were Col. Townsend Whelen, Phil Sharpe, and Earl Narramore, all authors who pioneered handloading literature and whose works are classics in the field today. A very important guy is Warrant Officer Frank W. Washam, U.S.M.C., with whom I jointly owned my first set of reloading tools, and who patiently endured my earliest efforts at writing about guns. Editor Neal Knox and publisher Dave Wolfe of *Handloader* magazine deserve special gratitude, as do several other editors—Alex Bartimo of *Shooting Times* and George Martin, then of *Guns and Ammo,* and others. These and many others helped to write this book without knowing it.

Most of all, my wife Jeannie must bear a part of the credit (or blame, as the case may be); she really wanted me to write the book, and has cheerfully made sacrifices over the last twenty years which have made it possible. In the final analysis, the publication of a book, especially a *first* book, is an event of much greater importance in the lives of the author and those who suffered through its creation with him than to any reader. These acknowledgments are, therefore, superfluous to all whose names do not appear in them, and I know it well. Still, every author has emotional debts, and I'm relieved to get them off my chest. For the rest of the shooting world, I can only contribute what follows, in the hope that it may be found useful.

John Wootters
Houston, Texas
October 1975

THE COMPLETE BOOK OF
PRACTICAL
HANDLOADING

1
Why Handload?

Handloading ammunition is the fastest-growing aspect of the shooting sports in the United States today. There was a time, not too many years ago, when a reloader was regarded as a practitioner of the occult, a dabbler in dangerous mysteries, and perhaps a bit of a nut, but the shooting public's attitude has changed. Today, to be a handloader is the "in" thing and is to be respected as a knowledgeable shooter with something of an edge over his non-reloading brethren. Perhaps a faint aura of mystery still clings to the handloading hobby (which this book may help dispel), but shooters are joining up literally by the millions.

Estimates place the number of active reloaders today at more than three million, in an annual rate of growth of that number of about 10 percent. These people assemble, and presumably fire, more than one *billion* rounds of ammunition each year, and spend about $50 million per year on their hobby. Handloading has come out of the dark ages!

There must be reasons for this wholesale enlistment in reloading's ranks, and there are—about as many different reasons as there are shooters. The one most commonly cited is economy, especially in this day of ever-increasing costs of everything, including ammunition. There's no doubt the reloader shoots more cheaply than his buddy who limits himself to factory-loaded ammo; a rifleman can assemble full-power hunting or target loads for about one-third the price of factory cartridges, while a shotgunner can save at least $1.50 per 25-round box of shells. Pistoleros do even better; by purchasing components in volume and casting their own bullets, they can fire their big-bore revolvers and autoloaders for about the same cost that they could shoot a .22 rimfire handgun.

Based on these figures, and varying according to the price of their reloading setup and the quantity of ammunition they shoot, reloaders can figure on amortizing the investment in tooling in anywhere from a few months to a year or two. This process can be hastened by joint ownership of the tools between two or more shooters. Several years ago, I helped five friends of mine set up a shotshell reloading press. They agreed on a single loading which would serve for informal clay-bird busting and upland bird hunting, and purchased shot by the hundreds of pounds, plastic wads by the thousands, and powder eight pounds at a whack. The press was mounted on a plywood base so that it could be moved from house to house and C-clamped to a kitchen table for use. The ammunition worked well in all the guns in which it was fired, and these fellows ground out 20-gauge cartridges by the tens of thousands at an aggregate cost of about a dollar per box, plus an evening's time every few weeks.

It should be added, however, that most shooters really don't save much money by reloading, for the simple reason that they shoot up their savings. People who handload shoot more, and thus it's probably more realistic to say that a novice handloader will get to shoot perhaps three times as much for the *same* cost, rather than that he'll save two-thirds on his cartridges.

This cutaway view illustrates the four components of a metallic cartridge: primer, powder, case, and bullet. Of the four, only the case is not expended in firing, and reuse of expensive brass cases is the foundation of the handloading hobby.

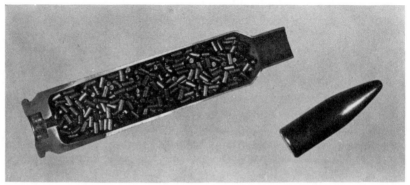

Serious clay-target shooters reload shotshells for economy, as do handgun competitors, but the ability of a reloader to make up light-kicking cartridges to introduce wife or kids to shooting is a unique advantage.

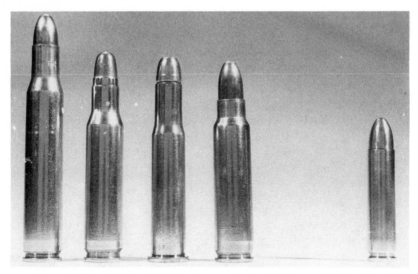

A facet of handloading that is often overlooked is the possibility of loading a cartridge to lower than normal velocities. Here, from left, the .30-06, .308 WCF, .30-30 WCF, and .300 Savage can all be loaded down to duplicate the ballistics of the little .30 M-1 Carbine at right.

There are other reasons for entering the reloading game. One of the best is that a loading tool can be used like the accelerator pedal on a car, to speed up (at least to some degree) or slow down the machine according to the specific need of the moment. At one time, one could purchase reduced-power loads in some calibers in factory ammo, but those days are gone forever. Nowadays, the shooter who confines himself to commercial ammunition has no choice but to run flat out, full throttle. Only by reloading can he adjust downward the power of his firearms.

So who wants to do a thing like that? Well, a man who has a young son or daughter coming along is wise to introduce the youngster to centerfire rifles or shotguns via light-kicking, quiet, reduced loads. They're more fun and less intimidating to shoot, the youngster is more likely to hit something (and thus enjoy himself earlier and more) and less likely to develop the dreaded flinch.

For that matter, there's no particular reason why a veteran shooter should have to use a full-power ammunition for paper-punching, plinking, and off-season practice. Such shooting is hardly ever at long range or at living targets which require a great deal of killing power, so why use more power than needed, especially when to do so is so much more expensive?

Certain kinds of wild game, in fact, are best shot with reduced loadings. In my home state of Texas, whitetail deer and wild turkey seasons

Shown here are four different approaches to a turkey load in the same .308 WCF cartridge. From left, a hard-alloy cast bullet, a 110-grain FMJ military bullet, a normal soft-point jacketed for game (not varmints), and a similar bullet loaded backwards. At correct velocities (around 2,000 fps) none of these will expand enough to be too destructive of a turkey dinner, and none are available to the shooter of factory ammunition.

run concurrently, and it's common to encounter turkeys while carrying a powerful centerfire rifle. With normal big-game loads, the hunter has his choice of passing up a turkey dinner or trying for a neck shot. Not even an expert can consistently bring off the neck shot on a gobbler at anything more than point-blank range, and if the bullet strays into the body the result is most depressing: a fine game bird wasted and a turkey dinner that looks as if it had been collected with a hand grenade.

The obvious and easy alternative, for a reloader, is a pocketful of specially prepared turkey loads, with nonexpanding bullets moving at very modest velocities. These loads can be made up for any deer rifle, and can usually be adjusted to conform with the same sight setting used for the full-power load. Three or four rounds of such special loads in my shirt pocket have produced tasty turkey dinners for me innumerable times when my chances of getting same with the big-game load in the chamber ranged somewhere between none and none whatsoever.

One can take this process even farther, loading down a deer-powered rifle for squirrel shooting, with home-cast bullets which destroy no more meat than a .22 rimfire. A chapter in this book is devoted to such loads.

That same deer rifle can, by handloading, be made even more versatile. A load adjustment may not make the rifle an ideal long-range varminter for shooting such pests as jackrabbits and woodchucks, but it may make it a surprisingly good one, and it's better than letting the rifle gather dust on the rack between big-game seasons. A set of reloading tools

Talk about versatility through handloading! Here are .45-70 loads with one ball for pests at short range, three balls for fun, a shot charge for snakes, a cast-bullet load duplicating factory ammo, a 350-grain hollowpoint for short-range deer, a 500-grain softpoint for big game, and a 500-grain "solid" for elephants—a lineup literally for everything from mice to moose and maybe dinosaurs!

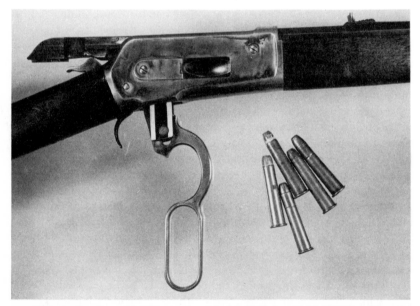

This is the fine old Winchester Model 1886 in .40-65 WCF caliber described in Chapter 20, together with five rounds of original factory ammunition. Reloading is the only way to enjoy firing such pieces today without undue risk of damaging the valuable rifle.

A principal advantage to handloading is the opportunity it gives you to select exactly the right bullet for any given purpose. The .250 Savage cartridge at right can be handloaded with any of the bullets shown, a couple of cast designs and jacketed slugs of 60, 75, 87, 100, 115, and 117 grains, in various shapes and types of construction.

is a lot cheaper than a second, special-purpose rifle, too, although I'd never deny a shooter his excuse to buy a new gun. Handloading can thus extend the versatility of a single rifle so that a hunter can enjoy it year round—which will produce remarkable results in terms of instinctive handling skills when that big whitetail begins busting brush in November. There is simply no substitute for *shooting* as a means of developing and maintaining shooting skills, and reloading makes it easy, fun, and cheap.

Some people get into reloading because Uncle Bill willed them a rifle for which they can't purchase commercial ammunition, perhaps a gun chambered to some foreign, rare, or obsolete caliber. Handloading is the only way to provide safe, efficient ammo for such a rifle, and almost any cartridge that ever achieved any degree of popularity anywhere in the world can be made up by a knowing reloader. Dies for making the cases and assembling the ammo are available, and suitable components can be bought or made. In many cases, if one wishes to shoot a certain war trophy rifle or an old buffalo gun, he *must* handload.

The same is true of what are called "wildcat" cartridges for rifles or handguns. These are nonstandard rounds which cannot be purchased in commercial form, a sort of design-it-yourself project for handloaders who have a ballistic itch they cannot scratch with anything offered by the major ammunition manufacturers. We'll have a lot more to say about wildcats in later chapters, but for now they must be added to the list of reasons for handloading.

I think one of the biggest—and most overlooked—advantages in handloading, at least for big-game hunters, is the ability to select precisely the correct bullet for the game and hunting conditions expected. Not that the commercial ammo makers don't load reliable bullets; they do, but their bullets must be compromises, attempting to suffice for anything from small whitetails in the thickets to pronghorns at 400 yards to bull elk across a mountain meadow. They do a surprisingly good job, but the conscientious handloader can do better.

Many new reloaders tell me their reasons for becoming involved in homemade ammo included expectations of increasing the range, power, and accuracy of their rifles and shotguns. Unfortunately, their expectations are often exaggerated. With patience and much experimenting, they may improve a shotgun's patterning, which translates to more game in the bag, but they will not substantially increase velocity or "power." The same is true of most modern rifle cartridges; accuracy can almost always be improved, often dramatically, but it may not be safely possible to soup up velocities. On the other hand, with some of the older cartridges such as the .257 Roberts, 7×57mm Mauser, or .30-06, very significant increases in velocity, trajectory flatness, and terminal energies are possible in perfect safety, provided a sound, modern rifle is used.

Serious accuracy fans, epitomized by the benchrest clan, are reloaders to a man, as are most varmint shooters. Again, the ammo factories make remarkably reliable and accurate ammunition, considering that they turn out cartridges by the millions which must function correctly in any rifle, from any maker in the world, to which those cartridges are adapted. The handloader, however, can determine the exact combinations of bullet, powder, primer, etc., which his individual rifle prefers, and then take all evening, if need be, to assemble 20 rounds to approximately *zero* tolerances. Since uniformity is the name of the accuracy game, it's not surprising that rifle accuracy is so amenable to improvement through reloading.

Most people who get into it discover that handloading ammunition is an absorbing and relaxing hobby in and of itself, rather than merely a means of feeding a rifle, pistol, or shotgun. It's a hobby without limits; one can simply pick a suitable load out of a loading manual and assemble quantities of it without further ado, or one can pursue handloading into the most rarefied realms of theoretical ballistics, concerning himself with J-factors, ballistic coefficients, expansion ratios, and other esoterica. And it's a satisfying game on every level. No engineering degree or grasp of differential calculus is required, but handloading appeals to many professionals with just such credentials.

A glance around the shooting club range will reveal that handloaders come from every aspect of American life. At one shooting bench, a Ph.D. may be taking lessons in reloading from a pipefitter, while a farmer, a doctor, and a ditchdigger look on and add their own commentary. Handloading is, by the way, historically a distinctively American pastime, although in recent years it's been spreading to a few other nations where the freedom to own sporting firearms and purchase components is not yet abolished.

Most serious handloaders are not only knowledgeable amateur ballisticians but also better-than-average marksmen, simply because they fire so many more rounds in a year than the fellows who buy commercial ammunition. They come to know their guns intimately and to understand their capabilities—and limitations—through long observation. All this makes them deadlier in the hunting field or on the target range, which is not a bad reason in itself for handloading.

You may have other reasons not mentioned here; as I said, there are as many excuses for buying that first reloading tool as there are reloaders. But the first, last, and best reason that I know of is simply that handloading, in all its varied aspects, is great recreation.

2

Basic Ballistics

It was noted in Chapter 1 that handloaders are amateur ballisticians, and indeed this is not a bad definition of the word "handloader." The process of assembling one's own ammunition either starts with a basic understanding of ballistics, or it eventually imparts that understanding through experience. Obviously, progress will be faster and satisfaction with one's home-brewed loads will be greater if the grasp of ballistics comes first. For that reason, let's take a look before we go any farther at the science of ballistics, which is the study of projectiles in motion.

The movement of a projectile is divided into three parts, dealing with *internal ballistics,* which takes place before the bullet or shot charge leaves the muzzle of the gun; *external ballistics,* which describes the projectile's flight from muzzle to target; and *terminal ballistics,* which has to do with the stopping of the bullet.

For purposes of simplification, we'll use terms dealing with the rifle, assuming that the parallel with shotgun ballistics will be clear to the reader.

When the firing pin of a breechloading rifle falls, it strikes the face of the primer cup, indenting it enough to crush the primer pellet against its anvil and detonate the mixture. Flame from this detonation passes through the flash hole in the bottom of the case's primer pocket and ignites the powder charge. Smokeless powder does not actually detonate, but burns very rapidly at a controlled rate, evolving large quantities of gas. This gas exerts pressure in all directions, but of the surfaces upon which it can apply force, the base of the bullet is the only one which can move. Actually, the brass walls and neck of the cartridge case can expand slightly, until stopped by contact with the steel of the chamber, and as the pressure from evolving powder gases increases they do exactly that, relaxing the tight grip by which the bullet was held in place in the neck of the cartridge.

Some few nanoseconds—as a billionth of a second is called—are required to overcome the inertia of the bullet and to start it on its journey down the barrel. For the first few fractions of an inch this movement is free, but the bullet then strikes the point at which the spiral lands and the grooves that make up the rifling originate. The rifling imparts a rotational movement to the bullet as it continues to accelerate up the bore under the still-increasing pressure of the gases now sealed behind it.

Shotshell pressures are determined by firing in a special gun which permits the powder gases to drive a piston that compresses a precision lead slug. Measurement of the shortened slug indicates pressure levels in LUP (lead units of pressure) which is not the same as pounds per square inch. Copper slugs are used for higher pressures in rifles and handguns.

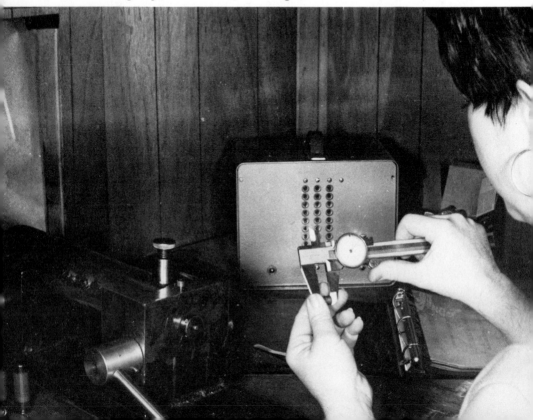

In most cartridges, this chamber pressure peaks by the time the bullet has moved a very few inches and it then drops fairly rapidly as the bullet continues to move, increasing the volume of the sealed system behind it. In modern, high-intensity rifles, peak pressures routinely run as high as 65,000 pounds per square inch absolute (PSIA). However, in most reloading references, another system of measurement is more common than pounds per square inch absolute, and this is called "crusher pressure." The technique for determining crusher pressure will be detailed later, but the units used are *copper units of pressure* (CUP) for rifles and handguns and *lead units of pressure* (LUP) for shotguns, in which normal peak pressures never exceed about 12,000 PSIA.

Although chamber pressures decline as the bullet moves along the bore of the gun, they remain high enough to impart continued acceleration to the projectile, and, in fact, the longer the barrel, within certain limits, the higher the muzzle velocity will be.

When the bullet departs the barrel, that phase of the process described as interior ballistics has ended. The bullet has been given a velocity, a kinetic energy, and it has been spun on its axis at a startling number of revolutions per minute (RPM) often exceeding 100,000 with ordinary hunting bullets. At this point it becomes a ballistic missile, unguided, and must contend with a whole new set of forces conspiring to slow it down, drive it off course, and pull it to earth. From here on, it's in the exterior-ballistics leg of its journey.

A projectile has a couple of physical properties with which the handloader must be familiar in order to understand exterior ballistics. The most basic of these is called *sectional density* (SD), which is a mathematical description of its weight as related to its cross-sectional area. Of two bullets with identical diameter and shape and composed of the same materials, the longer one has the high sectional density. The numerical expression of SD is derived by dividing the bullet's weight in pounds by the square of its diameter, in inches. Handloaders need not do the arithmetic often, however, since most bullet manufacturers publish the sectional densities of their products.

The importance of the SD concept is that the higher the sectional density, the harder the bullet is to stop and the more penetration it will achieve in any medium, if all else is equal, including air.

The second property of importance is called the bullet's *ballistic coefficient* (BC), and it is related to the sectional density. Essentially, the BC is a mathematical expression of the shape of the projectile, or, to put it another way, its streamlining. A bullet of high BC slips through the atmosphere more readily than one with a lower BC, and thus has a flatter

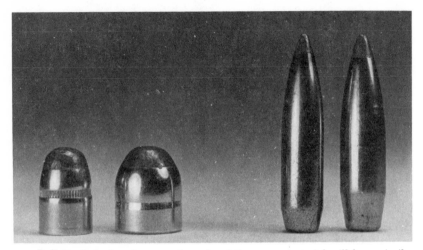

Bullets of similar shapes and made of the same material will have similar sectional densities, regardless of caliber. At left are a .38 125-grain roundnose and .45 200-grain bullet whose sectional densities are identical: .140. At right are a 7mm 160-grain boattail and a .30 190-grain boattail of nearly identical SDs— .284 and .286, respectively.

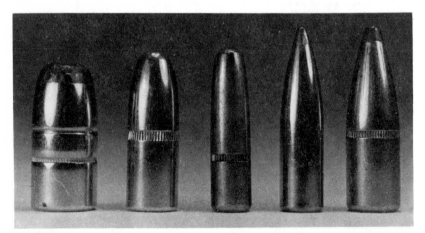

Despite different shapes and calibers, these bullets all have very similar sectional densities. They are (from left) a 400-grain .45 (SD .272), a 250-grain .35 (SD .279), a 154-grain 7mm (SD .273), a 180-grain .30 (SD .277), and a 270-grain .375 (SD .275)

These four bullets—all 180-grain .30 calibers—have identical sectional densities but vastly different ballistic coefficients, due to different shapes. From left, the roundnose's BC is .312, that of the flat-point .361, the spitzer's is .474, while the boattail's BC is .535. The higher the number, the more efficient the projectile in motion in a medium such as air.

These five bullets, despite their varied appearance and diameters, all boast very similar ballistic coefficients. They are, from left: 220-grain .35 (BC .299), 100-grain .270 (BC .291), 500-grain .45 (BC .297), 100-grain 6.5mm (BC .294), and 170-grain .32 (BC .291).

trajectory and more retained velocity and energy at any range, if initial velocities were the same.

Actually, the ballistic coefficient of a bullet describes its ability to overcome resistance relative to a standard, experimental projectile, and the numbers are derived by multiplying the sectional density by a form factor which describes the shape of its nose (and heel, in the case of boat-tailed bullets). A long, sharp point on a bullet gives it a higher BC than a blunt profile. A round ball, such as a shotgun pellet or a ball from a muzzle-loading rifle, possesses the poorest possible ballistic shape, as well as the lowest possible sectional density.

It must be apparent by now that SD and BC are critical to the hand-loader of rifle and pistol ammo, because they have everything to do with the performance of a bullet in flight.

As the projectile is launched from the muzzle, two things happen to it immediately. It begins to lose velocity as it encounters air resistance, and it begins to fall toward the center of the earth as the force of gravity is applied. The greater the initial velocity and the higher its ballistic coefficient, the farther from the muzzle it will get before these two factors bring it to earth. The rate of loss of velocity is at best quite rapid, and the bullet falls toward the center of the planet at exactly the same rate as it would if dropped from the same elevation with no forward motion at all.

However, although the loss of *velocity* is quite rapid, the loss of the bullet's rotational speed is negligible, and it strikes the target at any ordinary range with about the same RPM with which it left the muzzle. In fact, if fired straight up the bullet will come to a dead stop and fall back to earth, still spinning. This factor has little effect on exterior ballistics, but it does have an effect on the bullet's performance upon impact, which shall be examined in another chapter.

As a bullet flies toward the target, it is subject to a lateral force from any wind which may be blowing, and will drift away from its line of departure from the bore. The amount of lateral displacement of the point of impact depends upon the velocity and angle of the wind, of course, and upon the difference in time-of-flight (TOF) of the actual bullet under the actual atmospheric conditions fired and the theoretical time-of-flight of the same bullet when fired in a vacuum.

A .22 rimfire high-speed bullet fired in a crosswind may actually drift more than an identical bullet at standard velocity, because the faster slug happens to be supersonic while the standard-speed one is traveling below the speed of sound. The "lag time" (difference between actual TOF and TOF in a vacuum) is greater for the supersonic projectile, so the wind-drift is greater. It sounds very complicated, and indeed is, but the effect on the handloader is rather simple; just pick a bullet with the highest practical ballistic coefficient. Just as it will show less drop over a given range, so will it be less subject to wind-drift.

Gyroscopic stability of a bullet in flight is another aspect of exterior ballistics. The spin imparted to the bullet by the rifling tends to keep it flying point-forward. Proper stability depends upon the rate of rifling twist, muzzle velocity, and the length of the bullet itself. In general terms, a given rifling twist can be exactly right for only one style of bullet at one velocity, but from a practical viewpoint, a compromise twist can usually be made to stabilize a fairly wide range of bullet weights (lengths) at least adequately. A heavier (longer) slug requires a quicker twist than a lighter (shorter) bullet, and, if bullet weight remains the same, a lower velocity requires a quicker twist. Since overstabilization is a lesser sin than understabilization, most compromise twists tend toward the quicker side, at least in calibers where relatively heavy bullets are commonly used.

An example of this matter of rifling twist rate is found in the early results with two competitive cartridges, the .243 Winchester Center Fire (WCF) and the .244 Remington. Bullet diameter in the two calibers is the same, but the .243 rifles had a 1-turn-in-10-inch rifling rate because Winchester envisioned the round as a combination deer-and-varmint number and wished to stabilize the heavier bullets that might be employed on whitetails. Remington saw the .244 as a pure varminter, and produced rifles with a 1-turn-in-12-inch twist for best accuracy with the lighter slugs. Winchester's concept proved to be in agreement with that of the general public, and the .244 soon fell by the wayside in the marketplace, forcing Remington to discontinue chambering rifles for the .244 and reintroduce the identical cartridge under the designation 6mm Remington, in rifles with a 1-turn-in-9-inch rifling.

Other illustrations of the effect of twist rates and velocity: I have a 7×57mm Mauser custom rifle with a 1-turn-in-12-inch twist, extremely slow for this caliber. The most accurate load I've developed for the rifle features the 154-grain Hornady roundnosed bullet. But Hornady also makes a 154-grain spitzer bullet in this diameter which is considerably longer than the roundnose. Identical loadings with the sharp slug scatter bullet holes all over the target, even though the sole difference is in the length (not even the weight, in this case) of the two bullets. The longer one simply will not stabilize adequately in this slow twist.

I once tried to develop a low-velocity load in a certain wildcat rifle of 6.5mm caliber, using the Norma 139-grain full-jacketed target bullet. This is a long, sharp, boat-tailed slug, and there was a point below which I could not take the velocity without opening groups badly and producing oval-shaped bullet holes in the target paper, a sure sign that the bullets were wobbling or yawing upon impact. Accuracy was excellent at velocities of 2,600 feet per second (FPS) or better, but when I reduced the powder charge to produce speeds below that figure, results went quickly to hell. If I could have magically changed the twist rate in that barrel to a quicker one, no doubt I could have achieved the 2,000-FPS turkey load I was seeking.

Hopefully, these experiences will clarify the relationships between rifling twist rate, velocity, and bullet length, for they are important to the reloader.

An interesting sidelight on this matter of stability is that a bullet usually does not "go to sleep" or stabilize perfectly for quite a few yards after it has left the muzzle. This phenomenon is commonly seen when measuring muzzle velocities by firing through paper chronograph screens. The screens will show slightly oval holes, indicating the bullet was still yawing, yet the same bullet at 50 yards will print a perfectly round hole. Occasionally, this tendency will produce a handload that delivers better groups, in terms of minutes of angle (MOA), at 100 yards than at 25 yards. The tendency is most pronounced with fairly long, heavy bullets at moderate velocities.

The last stage in the bullet's journey, terminal ballistics, occurs after impact with the target. This area is of interest principally to hunters, since target shooters could hardly care less how hard their bullets strike the backstop after passing through the paper.

Upon arrival at the game animal, however, a hunting bullet still has most of its work to do. If the target is a groundhog, it must expand explosively and minimize ricochets. If it's a deer, both expansion and penetration are important, and if one is shooting at an African elephant, penetration is the supreme criterion of success. Much of this performance is built into the bullet itself, which will be dealt with later, but what makes the bullet work is the velocity, and resulting kinetic energy, it's carrying when it strikes. Kinetic energy (essentially the weight of the bullet multiplied by the square of its velocity) may or may not be a direct measurement of killing power; that has been the subject of argument for about a hundred years, but it does give us an adequate *comparative* measurement of various bullets at various velocities. Note the importance of velocity in that formula above; its *square* is used, which means that the faster it's traveling, the harder it hits. And that, I hope the reader will have realized before now, means that a slug with a high ballistic coefficient hits harder at any range than one with a lower BC.

The instant an expanding bullet strikes the body of an animal, its nose shape begins to change very rapidly, and with it the ballistic coefficient, since that number depends upon the bullet's form. Note now, though, that the sectional density changes only as the cross-sectional area of the nose becomes larger. If we assume for the moment that all expanding bullets expand at about the same rate and to the same degree upon impact with similar targets, we can see the importance of the basic sectional density characteristic. If all else is equal, the bullet with the highest sectional density will penetrate more deeply before coming to rest. In the case of non-expanding, steel-jacketed bullets for use on the heaviest African game, sectional density is almost a direct linear measurement of lethality if velocities are similar.

Bullet construction is the primary consideration in planning a hunting handload. These four .375 300-grain Bitterroots (shown with an unfired specimen) were all recovered from downed game. All retained more than 90 percent of their original mass for maximum penetration, yet all are expanded to at least double the original diameter for maximum tissue destruction and shock.

Kinetic energy is usually expressed in terms of foot-pounds, and that terminology (FP) will be used throughout this book. A bullet is carrying a certain number of foot-pounds of energy when it strikes, but it is also spinning, remember. A good deal of controversy has arisen over whether this rotational energy has a significant effect on a game animal, and some fairly hairy special rifles and cartridges have been put together to test the matter. But simple calculations can show that a bullet's spin, even if it stopped in the animal's body, could not apply more than four or five foot-pounds of energy, as contrasted to from 1,500 to 3,000 or more FP delivered by the forward motion of the same slug.

However, an often overlooked factor is that the spin of the bullet, which is practically undiminished at impact, represents very great centrifugal forces acting to help expand the bullet as its physical integrity is disrupted. For this reason, experiments in bullet expansion conducted by firing them into recovery media at reduced velocities to simulate long-range impacts must be regarded with suspicion, since slowing down the bullet also greatly reduces its RPM.

This has been a very simplified—some may say "oversimplified"—discussion of ballistics, but it may serve to relate certain important concepts in the beginning handloader's mind, and help him visualize all that takes place between the fall of the firing pin and the impact on target of the bullet.

Here, now, is the great secret to becoming a ballistician, without benefit of computers, sliderules, or laboratory equipment. All you really need is a nickel plastic ruler (which now costs 39¢), a rifle, and a batch of handloaded cartridges. You take all three out to the range and fire a group, holding dead center on the bull's-eye (with a properly zeroed rifle) at 100, 200, and 300 yards, and farther if possible. Then you walk up to each target and with the ruler you measure the distance between the group center and the center of the bull, and presto—you have determined the trajectory of your handload at least as accurately as any computer could have done it. If there was a wind blowing and you can make a fair estimate of its speed and angle, you will also have determined the "wind-bucking" qualities of the load, at least to the ranges fired.

If you wish, you can use the drop data you have accumulated to make a graphic plot of the trajectory on regular (not logarithmic) graph paper, compressing the scales for convenience by using one small square for five or ten yards horizontally and one inch vertically. Select a line-of-bore (sometimes called "line-of-departure") and plot the measured drops at the various ranges below it. Now you can sketch in the actual path of the bullet, either using a French curve or roughly freehand, and extrapolate it at least another 100 or so yards.

Next, draw a line-of-sight, beginning about 1½ inches above the origin of the line-of-bore, to represent the difference between the mounted scope and the axis of the bore, to cross your trajectory at whatever distance at which you intend to zero the rifle with at load. Now, you can actually measure the path of the bullet above or below the line-of-sight at any distance, remembering to measure perpendicular to the line-of-sight.

Since at least two popular reloading manuals include very comprehensive ballistics tables today, the above exercise may not be as valuable as it once was, but I still recommend it, especially to the new reloader, if only because it gives him such a clear mental image of a rifle's trajectory. He may be startled at just how rapidly even the flattest-shooting cartridge actually drops at hunting ranges, and he can use his ruler to play with various possible zero points to see how the trajectory can appar-

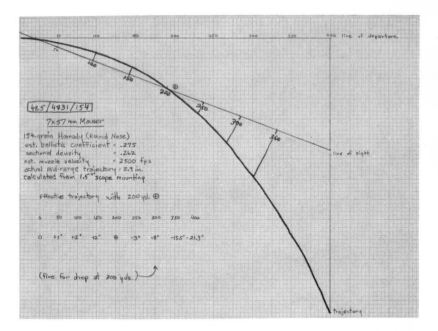

ently be flattened by proper sighting-in, and by the use of a telescopic sight. And if he goes to the trouble of constructing similar trajectory charts for blunt- and sharp-snouted bullets of the same caliber and velocity, he will see very graphically the value of a good ballistic coefficient.

Such charting can be done without actually firing a shot, through the use of a cardboard sliderulelike device called the Speer Ballistics Calculator. By following the simple directions with care, very accurate trajectory graphs can be drawn for bullets of various weights, BCs, and velocities. For example, one might determine that, in a given cartridge, a heavier bullet might be flatter-shooting at long ranges, due to its better BC, than a lighter slug even though the latter could be launched at much higher velocity. Such theoretical diddling can be fascinating, and, better than that, it can save a lot of money for components, and time on the target range and at the loading bench.

3

Planning the Load

There is no such thing as the perfect rifle, wife, automobile, or dog, and, unfortunately, neither is there such a thing as a perfect handload. Every combination of components which goes into a round of hand-loaded ammunition is necessarily a set of compromises. For example, maximum power and maximum accuracy in a rifle or pistol load usually work against each other, just as top velocities and optimum patterning do in a handloaded shotshell. The cheapest load is never the most efficient hunting load. The lowest-recoiling practice, plinking, and small-game load very rarely delivers a point of impact relative to the full-power big-game load which will permit the identical sight-setting. And so it goes; any handload represents a series of trade-offs, hopefully achieving a fairly close approach to the handloader's purposes as a final result.

There are several characteristics which must be juggled to achieve this end. In metallic (rifle and handgun ammunition) cases, some of them are: high velocity, which contributes to flatness of trajectory and high-impact energies; bullet selection, which contributes to the same things, plus accuracy and expansion on game; high accuracy; low cost; low-recoil and noise levels; and compatibility with a particular firearm. Or perhaps the reloader has acquired a large quantity of cases, bullets, or powder which he wishes to use up. Then of course, his purpose may be the opposite of *high* velocity; he may be seeking a *specific* velocity level ranging from a few hundred feet per second to perhaps 2,000 FPS, as in the afore-mentioned turkey load.

In shotshells, we have to try to balance velocity and patterning per-centages in a given gun's choke against costs and another factor not en-countered much in loading metallic ammo: production speed and ease. Rifle cartridges for hunting or target are rarely assembled in batches of more than 20 to 60 rounds at a sitting, and varying components doesn't alter the rate at which the batch can be completed. But shotgun shells are expended in much greater numbers, whether on clay targets or game birds, and most handloaders of shotshells measure their production rates in terms of boxes per hour. Some loading tools are capable of producing many hundreds of cartridges per hour.

Such an output, however, demands standardization of components, especially wads, and most such tools are set up strictly for the one-piece plastic wad columns which incorporate an over-powder sealing cup, a spacing and cushioning element, and a shot-protector cup, all in the same unit. A reloader with a specific purpose in mind for a given load may very well discover that these plastic wads, while convenient and fast, do not deliver the exact performance he is seeking. Instead, he'll choose to put together a "built-up" wad column composed of several separate pieces. This means making many more hand motions in loading a single car-tridge, and cutting his production rate to half or less of the rounds per hour his tool is capable of producing. Again, he has to decide upon his priorities; is the gain in performance worth an extra evening or two at the loading bench?

Although experienced reloaders know of these necessary com-promises, it's amazing how few of them take the trouble to solve the problem in the quickest and most satisfactory manner—unless they hap-pen to be professional engineers and thus accustomed to the process of sitting down and writing out a set of specifications!

This should be the first step in developing any sort of handload for any kind of gun. The idea is that you can't know when you've arrived if you don't know exactly where you wanted to go in the first place.

For illustration, let's examine the case of a hunter who plans his first hunt for pronghorn antelope in Wyoming and intends to use his own handloads (naturally!). He figures that he has to be prepared for a very long shot at a target no bigger than the average whitetail deer. Further-more, since that target is a living creature, it's crucial that the bullet be capable of humane execution. His rifle is chambered for the .270 WCF cartridge, one of the best for such shooting.

This fellow (let's call him Joe) can nose around in the reloading manuals and pick a load formula at random, hoping it'll work on antelope, or he can go about it in a bit more organized fashion, selecting his performance criteria in advance and deciding on the compromises he's willing to make to achieve his goals.

First comes bullet selection, as it nearly always does regardless of the purpose of the load. It must be a bullet designed for big game; obviously, a non-expanding target bullet or one intended to explode on a jackrabbit is unsuitable. Second, it must be a bullet with a high ballistic coefficient, to flatten the trajectory and retain high terminal energy at long range. Third, it must be accurate in his particular rifle at more or less maximum velocities, and, fourth, its weight should be such that it can be given adequate velocity. A tall order? You bet, but that's one of the virtues of this handloading business; such bullets exist, and can be found by the reloader for almost any set of specifications. The beginner may be bewildered by the vast array of .270 slugs on the market today, but the chances are the reloader with a little experience already has some "book" on bullets of various makes in his own rifles. In any case, let's say Joe decides on the 130-grain Hornady Spire Point bullet for his antelope load. This one meets all his requirements, plus it has a reputation for slightly better than average expansion at long ranges where velocities have dropped below normal. Whether it will be accurate in his particular .270 cannot be predicted; all rifles are individuals and only testing can determine their tastes in bullets. Assuming the Hornady passes that test, the load planning can proceed. The bullet/rifle combination must be capable of hitting an antelope in the vital chest area with every shot at, say, 300 yards with a perfect hold, and that means grouping within about a 12-inch circle at that particular range.

That's really not a very demanding standard in fact; most combinations should do twice that well, but it gives Joe a specific way of knowing when his handload has achieved the accuracy necessary for his upcoming hunt in Wyoming.

With the bullet selection finished, Joe interests himself in velocity, since this will be his only other key to flatness of trajectory and terminal energy. In this case, the more the better. He can peek into the Hornady *Handbook of Cartridge Reloading*, Vol. II, and discover that the 130-grain slug can be launched at about 3,200 FPS from a 24-inch barrel. He can then turn to page 432 of that same handbook, in the ballistics tables, and read off the flight characteristics of this bullet at this velocity. The drop figures presented here are drop below *line-of-sight*, and therefore represent actual bullet path. He will see that if he zeroes the load at 200

Random assembly of handloads "out of the book" may produce satisfactory ammo, but it's best to have a specific purpose (even a specific hunt or species) in mind when writing loading specs.

yards, his bullet will be 1.3 inches high at 100 yards and 6.1 inches low at 300. If he zeroes at 300 yards, his slug will be 3.4 inches high at 100 yards and 4.1 inches high at 200, dropping 9.9 inches at 400 yards. If he intends to limit his shooting at an antelope buck to about 300, it's obvious that this bullet at this velocity has plenty of trajectory for a clean kill without much, if any, holdover at any range.

Since these same figures are given for the same bullet at all feasible velocities, he can also determine the trajectories which will result if he fails to achieve the full 3,200 FPS suggested by the loading data.

At this point, the load is taking final shape on paper. Joe has the right bullet in mind, and knows the velocity range within which it will deliver the desired performance if he does his part in aiming and squeezing.

Now for the compromises. Cost, recoil, and muzzle blast will be traded off in a serious big-game hunting load for the necessary trajectory, power, and accuracy.

The criteria for this particular load are fairly simple. Joe must achieve at least a 12-inches-at-300-yards grouping with the Hornady bullet, and he wants a velocity at close to 3,200 FPS as is practical and safe in

Pre-planning a handload via written specifications is even more important than usual when that ammunition is to be fired at dangerous game, like this African Cape buffalo shot by the author (right) in Mozambique.

his rifle. If he can beat that accuracy figure, so much the better, because it will allow for a little more aiming error in the excitement of the hunt, but he has avoided adoption of some such vague description as "good enough" by writing down his specs before sitting down at the loading bench. The actual development and testing of the load will be detailed in a later chapter.

In the meantime, let's take a look at the problems of Joe's buddy, Jack, whose ship has come in and who is planning an African safari.

Jack has in mind busting a couple of Cape buffalo, an elephant, and maybe a lion, and he has bought a rifle chambered for the .458 Winchester Magnum cartridge. It will be apparent that Jack's concerns are wholly different from Joe's since the heavy, dangerous game is always shot at the closest possible range, and since these beasts are not easy to stop even with the mighty .458. Jack's accuracy standards will not be high—say, minute-of-buffalo, instead of minute-of-angle—but he is preoccupied with delivering the very maximum of smashing power possible, and prepared to sacrifice everything else for it, including cost, pleasant recoil sensation, and muzzle blast. Since he will probably wish to use soft-point bullets on the lion and will surely choose the so-called "solid" full-metal-cased ones for elephant, he will write into his specifications that both types of bullets have the same point of impact with the same sight setting.

He might go again to Hornady, who makes 500-grain .458 bullets of both types (I am aware of no other custom bulletmaker, except Colorado Custom Bullets, who does). Almost his sole interest in testing will be development of maximum short-range energies, and a similar point of impact of both bullet styles. As always, the more accuracy, the better, but Jack will not trade off 1,000 foot-pounds of energy for an inch better grouping at 100 yards. A Cape buffalo is a big target, compared to Joe's pronghorn, and the buff is quite likely to shoot back if not walloped properly with the first round.

Another reloader, John, couldn't care less about Cape buffalo, but gets his kicks from clobbering groundhogs at extended ranges. For this purpose, he has acquired a new, heavy-barreled .22-250 Remington rifle with a 24-power scope. Let's see how he writes his load specs.

First, last, and always, the varminter is after accuracy. He may write down a minimum requirement of one-inch groups at 100 yards, perhaps even smaller since he'll be shooting at much smaller targets at up to the same ranges at which Joe plans to smack his antelope. John will sacrifice all else (except safety) for accuracy.

Other elements, however, are very important to the varmint shooter. He needs the flattest possible trajectory, and also the smallest possible wind-drift characteristics in order to score consistently. He also prefers minimum recoil because he knows that any rifleman can do better precision shooting when he isn't being belted every time he pulls the trigger, and minimum muzzle blast because loud reports make farmers nervous, and farmers have the woodchucks John likes to shoot on their property. For the same reason, John is concerned about ricochets; bouncing bullets, whining across the landscape, make farmers extremely nervous.

Again, bullet selection comes first. John may discover that his new rifle does best with Speer's 52-grain hollow-point bullet, or perhaps Nosler's Solid Base slug of the same weight. These are famed for accuracy and reliable blow-up upon impact, although by no means the only ones on the market which have such reputations.

John Varminter must now begin to compromise. If he knows his business, he will not be surprised to discover that he receives the very finest of giltedged accuracy with the bullet moving at something less than maximum muzzle velocity, and he trades off a bit of trajectory for an increment of accuracy, getting a slightly lighter recoil sensation and a bit less blast into the bargain. Power is of no importance to John, whereas it was of supreme importance to Jack, the safarist.

And so it goes. Another reloader may want a turkey load for his deer rifle. He'll need a bullet that will not expand and a muzzle velocity of about 1,800 to 2,000 feet per second, plus a point of impact that is at least usable with the standard zero of his rifle with the big-game load.

Another man who has a boy coming along and wants to do a lot of off-season practice shooting is likely to put economy at the top of this specification list. He'll pick a cast bullet which he molds himself, and choose a powder charge that not only delivers moderate velocity (and kick and blast) but that allows him to extract more rounds of ammunition from a pound of powder. He'll have to give up a bit of accuracy, more than likely, and will surely have to change his sight setting, but that's an easy compromise. He'll get to shoot maybe 100 rounds for the price of a box of 20 factory cartridges, plus a little more work in making his own bullets.

A shotgunner will, of course, have an entirely different set of criteria for his proposed handload, and a somewhat different set of compromises to make. Velocity is not so critical in shotshells, within broad limits, but patterning is of supreme importance. This is where the written specifications list will start with most shotshell reloads.

A goose hunter will want 80 percent or better patterns for killing effectiveness at long range, whereas the quail hunter is looking for wide, uniform patterns with small shot at 30 yards. The target shooter loads his practice ammo for maximum density and uniformity at the ranges at which he breaks his clays, but he'll shoot so many of these loads that the price per shell and production rate can become important to him.

A father who wants to introduce his offspring (male or female; girls love to shoot, too!) to the joys of scattergunning will be wise to load light shot charges at very moderate velocities to reduce recoil to a minimum for early training. He always wants the best available patterns, just as any rifleman always likes to see smaller groups than his specs called for, but Dad will gladly trade pattern efficiency in this case for soft recoil and an enthusiastic young shotgunner.

The important lesson is that any handload should be carefully thought out in advance, regardless of its purpose or the type of firearm in which it will be fired. This need not necessarily be done on paper, but I often find that it helps clarify my thinking to do so, especially with loads in which two or more characteristics are almost equally important and a balance of performance levels must be struck. Otherwise, the process of developing and testing a new load has a way of wandering off into irrelevant channels or focusing upon features of the load which do not really count in its overall efficiency.

This results, usually, in a great deal of time being wasted both at the bench and on the range, not to mention the cost of components expended to no particular purpose. Furthermore, launching a load-development project without specific criteria can lead to a futile effort to maximize *all* performance characteristics, and becloud the necessity of making intelligent compromises.

Worst of all, failing to plan a load in specific terms deprives the handloader of the sense of accomplishment which comes with realizing that the goal has been achieved, and, as I said before, you can't know when you've arrived if you don't know where you were supposed to be going. Planning a handload is like marking off a mental road map, detailing not only the destination but the route by which you expect to get there. In the long haul, "planning your load and loading your plan" is sure to add greatly to your reloading pleasure.

4

Brass

When you hear a reloader use the word "brass," he's usually referring to the cartridge cases in which he assembles his handloads. These cases are made of brass, as a matter of course, although various other metals such as steel and aluminum have been employed experimentally or in wartime when brass supplies were critical.

Because rifle and pistol cases are entirely of brass, they are called "metallic" cases. Actually, shotshell cases were once made of brass, too, but such items are rarely reloaded today. Modern shotshells are of paper or plastic, with or without some metal portions, and they are not considered metallic cases. At this point it's best to separate metallic and shotshell reloading, and the next several chapters shall be devoted to the metallics. In general, what is said of rifle cases also applies to those used in revolvers and pistols. The differences will be made clear in the chapters on handgun reloading.

Cartridge brass is an alloy composed of about 70 percent copper and 30 percent zinc. Some common American brands may reveal a trace of silver, and alloy proportions may vary by a few tenths of a percent. The reloader may encounter many handgun cases and a few rifle cases with a plating of nickel, but they're still brass and are treated as such in all reloading procedures.

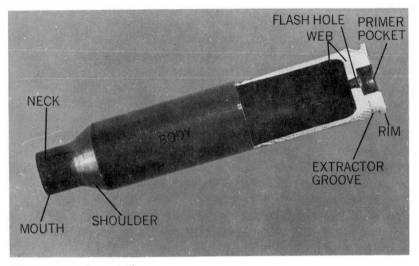

The anatomy of a cartridge case.

A brass case has two fundamental jobs to do. It provides a durable and convenient package in which the other components of a cartridge are contained and may be stored and handled safely and easily, and it seals the breech of the firearm against the rearward escape of powder gases during firing. It performs the latter task by expanding as the chamber pressure mounts and clinging to the walls of the chamber tightly enough to prevent gases from flowing backward around the case.

It was the discovery of the ability of brass to do these jobs that made practical the first successful breechloading firearms and, of course, the earliest repeaters other than muzzle-loading revolvers. Although metals technology has made fantastic strides during the century or so in which brass has been used for centerfire cartridge cases, no other material has ever been discovered that does the same jobs so well and so cheaply, and the general characteristics of the brass case have changed little since the universal adoption of Boxer primers in this country.

It should be added that the use of brass cases made handloading possible, since the case itself is changed very little in the process of firing. It is the only one of the components of a cartridge that is not consumed or expended when the cartridge is fired, and this is fortunate, since the case is by far the most costly of those components. The ability to reuse the case five, ten, or fifty times is the principal source of the savings on ammunition possible through handloading. When a shooter of factory ammunition ejects an empty case and leaves it lying on the ground, it is as though he took 12 to 18 cents (depending on the cartridge) out of his pocket and pitched it into the grass. That's why chronic reloaders get sore backs from sniping discarded cases on a public range. Professional hunters in Africa tell me that they have trouble, with reloading American clients, getting the hunters to deliver the quick follow-up shots so necessary on dangerous game because of their habit of opening a rifle bolt slowly enough to catch the case as it's extracted. I have the same habit, and it's a hard one for a handloader to break.

Brass as an alloy has several characteristics which make it well suited to use in cartridge cases. Its tensile strength is high enough to withstand the gas pressures generated in rifle cases when properly supported by the chamber and bolt, and yet it can be formed by extrusion, milling, and stamping for economical fabrication. It is elastic enough to expand and seal the breech of a gun, and still springy enough to break that seal so that it can be extracted. To put that another way, brass is elastic enough to firmly hold a bullet forced into a cartridge case neck, and yet soft enough to be expanded by gas pressure to release that bullet at the correct instant. It is easily worked in simple reloaders' dies, not only to prepare it for its next loading but to be changed into a completely different configuration if desired.

Like all metals, brass has a grain structure which can be made visible under high magnification (about 150×) with proper polishing and etching. This microstructure can be changed by either cold-working or annealing (heat-treating), and indeed *is* changed with every reloading operation on the case. When the microstructure changes, so do the physical properties, especially those of hardness and elasticity (springiness). A cartridge case must have three different degrees of hardness and springiness in various portions of its anatomy, in fact, to perform as it should. The head portion, the first half-inch or so forward from the primer end, must be very hard, while the neck is considerably softer. The crystalline structure of the alloy is much larger in the head and relatively smaller in the neck. The body of the case falls between the two extremes, not as hard as the head section and much harder than the neck.

The reason is that these segments of the case have different jobs to do. The head must be strong enough to support the tremendous pressures generated by powder gases without rupturing. The neck must be soft enough to grip the bullet and to expand upon firing, while the midsection of the case needs an intermediate hardness.

Cold-working the brass, which happens when it is resized after firing, tends to enlarge the crystalline structure of the metal and make it harder.

When it becomes too hard, the neck of the case, which receives the most severe cold-working, will crack or split, and this is probably the greatest cause of lost cases for most reloaders. It can be avoided by re-heat-treating the case necks, as described in the following chapter.

If the annealing process is carried too far and the head area of the case is allowed to become too hot, it will be softened enough to ruin it, since its ability to withstand high pressures will have been destroyed. Once in a very long while a batch of factory cases with soft heads may get into commercial distribution, or even one or two cases in a batch can exhibit this defect. I haven't encountered such a problem in commercial brass for more than ten years, and then it was under a European label. Actually, the reloader doesn't have to deal with this matter of brass hardness very often, and it isn't as complicated as it may sound, but it's essential that he understand the basic physics of the question in order to understand certain other matters. To put it simply, the more a cartridge case is used, the more brittle the thin brass sections tend to become, especially in the neck and shoulder areas. This tendency can be reversed by annealing, but the application of heat to any cartridge case must be carefully controlled, lest those sections that must be hard and tough become soft. I will discuss this further when describing specific reloading procedures.

It will have become apparent by now that the strength of a firearm is to some degree the strength of the cases fired in it, since the brass case is the weakest link in the mechanical structure of a gun. At the moment of firing, the case actually becomes an integral element in the gun itself, and if it fails, the gun fails. Since brass is weaker than steel, the question arises as to how the case is able to stand the pressures of firing. Very simply, the answer is that those pressures are applied over so short a span of time that the brass literally hasn't time to yield before the stress drops back within tolerances. If this sounds strange, note that the temperatures developed within a rifle chamber at the instant of firing are not only far in excess of the melting point of brass but also higher than the melting point of the steel of which the arm is made, yet neither brass nor steel melts simply because these temperatures are applied so briefly.

We're talking about *normal* temperatures and *normal* pressures now; if chamber pressures rise far above normal limits, the brass case will be permanently deformed and ruined. The diameter of the case head, rim, or belt may be enlarged and the primer pocket so expanded that a primer will drop out of it. In extreme cases, the brass may be so swollen within its chamber that it cannot be extracted by the rifle's mechanisms, but in such cases some damage is usually done to the weapon itself. If all this suggests to you that case life upon repeated loadings and firings is an indication of the pressures developed, you're a most perceptive reader; if dies and chamber are normal and cases begin to fail at the second or third firing, chances are pressures are much too high for continued use even though the gun is not damaged. One of the characteristics of cartridge brass is, then, an ability to serve as a sort of early warning system for re-loaders who tend to bite off more than their rifles can chew.

If the warnings are ignored and pressures pushed even higher, the reloader will eventually see the results of a case failure, and I guarantee that he'll be impressed. The damage done depends upon the type of arm, but, typically, a tremendous quantity of high-temperature, high-pressure gas rushes back through the rifle's action, often wrecking it. Locking lugs will be set back, the extractor blown off, the magazine blown out, the stock demolished, and quite often the man holding the rifle will be injured. The fact that I've never heard of a bolt being blown completely out of the receiver or a handloader killed is a tremendous compliment to the design and strength of modern rifles. I know of cases where shooters lost the sight in one or both eyes and suffered serious injury to the hand and arm supporting the gun's forearm, however, which is reason enough to understand the capabilities—and limitations—of the brass cartridge case. Reloading safety begins with a due respect for those limitations; forget that and you're walking the razor's edge between pleasure and disaster.

An important mechanical aspect of a cartridge case is its system of headspacing. Remember that word, *headspace*; you'll hear it and read it a lot in discussions of handloading.

The gap between the jaws of this caliper represents *maximum* allowable headspace, .006 inch, in centerfire metallic cartridges. More headspace than this may create a hazardous situation, while less may cause hard chambering.

Headspace may be defined as the amount of forward-and-backward movement of a chambered case which is possible when the breech is closed and locked. Ideally, this end play should be zero, but this is impractical in factory ammunition because of manufacturing tolerances in both cartridges and chambers. Therefore, industry standards set allowable headspace at .004 inch *maximum*. Four one-thousandths of one inch is not a great deal of space, but more headspace than this in a chambered cartridge is considered excessive and potentially dangerous.

Headspace is controlled by some part of the cartridge case being contacted and stopped by a corresponding surface within the chamber as the round enters. Four systems of headspacing are in common use in sporting arms today. The commonest, at least in rifle cartridges, is the *rimless* case, typified by such rounds as the .30-06, .270, .243, and a host of others, which are said to headspace on the shoulder. These are stopped as they enter the chamber by contact with the shoulder at a point at which the case shoulder has a certain specified diameter, and the headspace is measured from a plane through the shoulder at this point to the face of the base head. Another popular system involves the *belted* magnum cases, which headspace on the belt around the case head just forward of the extractor cannelure. Theoretically, this is supposed to be a very precise method of controlling headspace, since the distance from the case-head face to the front face of the belt is quite small. In practice, however, it ain't so.

The third system has to do with *rimmed* cases, and is used with most of the old black-powder cases in rifles, the .30-30 and .45-70, many revolver rounds including the .38 Special, .357 Magnum, .41 Magnum, and .44 Magnum. It is also the only system used in headspacing shotshells, although headspace is much less critical in shotguns because of the lower pressures involved. In rimmed cases, the forward movement of the case in chambering is stopped by contact between the front face of the rim and a recess cut in the chamber for the purpose. The headspace measurement on rimmed cases is, therefore, the thickness of the rim itself. This is probably the most precise method of headspacing in use today, although it's also the oldest.

The fourth system is used for rimless, *straight* cases which have no shoulder, and these are said to headspace on the mouth of the case. The only rifle cartridge using this method is the .30 M-1 Carbine round. A few semiautomatic pistol cartridges such as the .45 ACP, 9mm Luger, and .380 also headspace on the mouth. With these, the depth to which the cartridge can enter the chamber is controlled by a recess in the chamber which contacts the mouth of the case, and the headspace measurement is

The four common methods of headspacing cartridges are represented here. From left to right, the .30 M-1 Carbine (headspaces on the *mouth*), the .243 WCF (headspaces on the *shoulder*), the .224 Weatherby Magnum (on the *belt*), and the .30-30 WCF (on the *rim*).

the full length of the case itself. Such cartridges cannot be crimped onto their bullets, since this will change the headspace.

Two modern cartridges, the .220 Swift and .225 WCF, are called *semirimmed* rounds. They have a sort of rim, but happen to headspace on the shoulder exactly as do all rimless cases.

The handloader is wise to get into the habit of thinking of "headspace" as relative to both the specific firearm in question and the cartridge. The cartridge can be of normal dimensions, but if the chamber itself is too long, the combination has excess headspace. Similarly, the chamber can be normal and still exhibit excess headspace with an individual cartridge which happens to be too short in the headspace measurement. In working with one particular rifle, the handloader can adjust his dies to produce cases which approach zero headspace in that rifle. He can also adjust belted magnum cases to headspace on the shoulder like rimless ones rather than on the belt, and reap certain benefits. All these things will be explained in Chapter 11.

Another mechanical characteristic of brass cases is the shape of their combustion chambers. A good deal of controversy has raged around the gunshop hot stoves about the importance of this shape in internal ballistics. The whole line of Weatherby magnum cartridges has what are called venturified shoulders, with distinct radii where neck and body meet the shoulder proper. This was claimed as an advantage in the earliest days of Weatherby promotion, but I've heard no such claims in recent years. Many ballisticians have long felt that a very sharp, abrupt shoulder contributed to better burning, especially of the slower powders, and it has finally been demonstrated scientifically that this is really true, although the advantage is quite small.

It has also been proved that cases with extreme body taper transfer more thrust from powder gases to the bolt face, stressing the locking system more heavily than do relatively straight-sided cases. Some taper is necessary, however, for proper feeding from magazine to chamber and for extraction.

Excessive body taper in a cartridge case eases extraction but reduces potential powder capacity and increases stress on the rifle's locking system. At left are three such cartridges, the .348 WCF, 6.5x58R, and .280 Ross. At right, three very straight-sided cases, the .300 Weatherby Magnum, .35 Whelen Improved (wildcat), and .284 WCF.

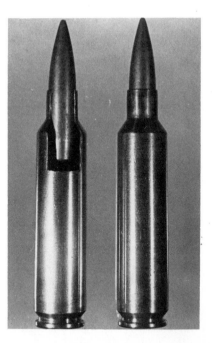

The cutaway case at left reveals how much of the powder capacity of a short-necked case can be occupied by the base of a long, heavy bullet when loaded to standard factory length.

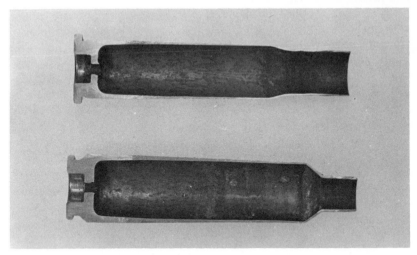

Body taper and shoulder angle control internal powder capacity and the shape of the combustion chamber. The .30-30 (top) exemplifies considerable taper and a very gentle shoulder, while the .284 WCF (below) illustrates minimum taper and very sharp shoulder.

Neck length of cases plays its role, too. Many modern magnum (and some non-magnum) rounds have been designed with very short necks, or, rather, very long bodies relative to overall length, in order to get more powder into a cartridge which will work through standard, .30-06-length actions. The 7mm, 6.5mm, and .350 Remington Magnums and .300 Winchester Magnum are classic, horrible examples. For short-action rifles, the .300 Savage, .243 WCF, and .308 WCF are just as bad. Short necks are one of the banes of the reloader. One reason is that it's difficult to make them grip a bullet firmly enough to resist displacement under recoil. Factory cartridges can be stab-crimped to hold the bullet in place for the single firing for which they're made, but reloaders are limited to the roll or taper crimp methods, and short necks create problems. The custom bullet-making firm of Nosler once offered a series of bullets especially cannelured for use in the .300 Winchester Magnum cartridge, since the Nosler design in use at that time simply couldn't be made to work with this short-necked case. Another problem with short necks arises when the handloader tries to seat a very long, heavy bullet. If the magazine is short, limiting overall loaded-cartridge length, the base of the bullet may protrude so deeply into the powder space inside the case that full ballistics cannot be realized. This was a particular problem with the .350 Remington Magnum in the short-actioned Model 600M carbine.

There is also some evidence that short necks detract from accuracy unless special handloading procedures—procedures few hunters employ—are used. In summary, short necks on cartridge cases are bad news for handloaders. Unfortunately, many very popular cartridges were so designed and we simply have to live with them, but any reloader who gets used to working with such rounds as the .257 Roberts, 7 × 57mm Mauser, .25-06 Remington, .270 WCF, or .30-06 will learn to curse the geniuses who designed such neckless wonders as the .223 Remington, .243 WCF, 7mm Remington Magnum, and others mentioned above.

The final mechanical element of the case which must be considered by the handloader is the design of the web, which is the term given to the solid sections of brass in and just in front of the head. This is most easily visualized in the accompanying photographs, which make it obvious that certain web designs are inherently stronger than others. The web, along with the aforementioned temper, or hardness, of the brass alloy, determines the ultimate strength of the case, which, in turn, represents the ultimate strength of the firearm itself. For the most part, cases of recent manufacture are well designed, more than adequate to contain the maximum pressures that reasonable handloaders demand of them. It is possible, however, that an occasional batch of old cases, in .44 Special, .45

From a reloader's point of view, too short necks on cases can be considered design faults in cartridges. The two at left, .300 Savage and .300 Winchester Magnum, exhibit this fault in spades. The two at right, the .30-06 and the .30-30 WCF, have ample necks.

Long Colt, and others, may be found which do not have a solid web at all, being of the folded-head or balloon-head style used decades ago. With good, virgin brass available today in these calibers, there's no point in using the old cases. Retire them; they're relics of the past and have no place in the practical handloading scene. If in doubt, simply section them lengthwise with a hacksaw.

A case is designed to work at a certain pressure level, and the use of recommended charges of the proper powders will achieve these pressures without exceeding their built-in safety margins. However, now and then a wildcatter gets a brainstorm about necking this or that up or down to produce his personal dream round. There's nothing wrong with this, except that he should make certain *before* he spends his dough for a custom barrel and loading dies that the webbing in his chosen case is designed for the pressures he anticipates in the final, wildcat version. A parent case designed to work at 45,000 PSIA will still be a 45,000-PSIA case even when altered in a wildcatter's dies to some new, exotic shape, and will surely give trouble if he tries to operate it at 60,000 PSIA. Wildcatting almost

These five cases include all major casehead types: from left, belted, rebated-rimless, rimless, rimmed, and semi-rimmed. Note differences in the amount and distribution of metal in the case heads, differences which affect the relative strengths of the various types.

never changes the *head* of the case, and that's where the basic strength of the brass case is.

And, by the way, research has pretty well demonstrated that there is no fundamental difference in the ultimate strengths of the modern rimless and belted cases. Due to differences in hardness and web thickness, it's possible to find a lot of rimless stuff which will stand more pressure than a given lot of belted brass, or vice versa. But, overall, the two types of cases are equal in ultimate strength, regardless of rumors to the contrary. Perhaps it's academic from the handloader's point of view, but the strongest case in manufacture today is probably a semi-rimmed number, the semi-obsolete .220 Swift.

Brass is the starting point for all reloading operations. Everything depends upon it—safety, mechanical functioning, and, as we shall see, much of the accuracy and power we can crank out of our rifles through reloading. Now, having examined the various metallurgical and physical characteristics of brass (in both handloading senses of the word), let's proceed to the actual operations involved in converting empty cases into live rounds of ammunition.

5

Case Preparation

Many shooters tend to think of a cartridge case as little more than a package, a sort of little brass bottle whose principal function is to hold all the "working" components of the load in proper relationship to each other prior to firing, and to be discarded afterwards. As we have seen in Chapter 4, there's quite a bit more to a cartridge case than that, and we shall see in this chapter that the case is important, even crucial, to the correct and safe functioning of the ammunition.

All cases manufactured anywhere in the world for a given caliber conform to precise specifications in external dimensions. This is assured by an organization known as the Sporting Arms and Ammunition Manufacturers Institute, usually referred to as SAAMI. When a manufacturer introduces a new cartridge, engineering drawings and specifications are placed on file with SAAMI, detailing cartridge and chamber dimensions, working pressures, and other data. This information is available to all other members of the Institute. By this means, .30-06 ammunition manufactured by, say, Norma of Sweden, C-I-L of Canada, or Federal of the U.S. will chamber and function safely in rifles made by Remington, Winchester, Sako, or any other SAAMI subscriber. That this is true is remarkable, considering the extremely small tolerances to which ammunition must be fabricated, but it is true, and shooters and handloaders benefit greatly from this system of standardization.

We take it for granted, even without thinking about it, that any cartridge which comes out of a box marked ".30-06 Springfield" will work in any rifle whose barrel is similarly marked, regardless of the brand name or even the nationality of the maker.

As a sidelight, this is the reason that certain cartridges' performances can be materially improved through reloading, while others cannot. Once standardized, pressure and velocity specifications are never changed. Therefore, cartridges such as the .257 Roberts, .30-06, 7×57mm Mauser, and others which were developed and standardized in an earlier era when modern progressive powders were not available and rifle actions may not have been as strong, are forever limited to pressures and velocities which may be safely exceeded in today's arms. The manufacturers may not exceed those specs in factory-loaded ammo, but handloaders working with sound modern weapons are free to maximize the ballistic potential of those cases in perfect safety.

On the other hand, cartridge designs which have been standardized within the last 20 years or so, including the very popular .243 WCF, 7mm Remington Magnum, and others, have pressure and velocity specifications which already take advantage of the best of today's components and firearms. In fact, since ammunition makers are not limited to powders which are sold for handloaders and may use special propellants not available over the counter to you and me, it's sometimes difficult to even equal the performance (in terms of velocities) of factory rounds without exceeding sensible pressure maximums.

However, although *external* brass dimensions are standard throughout the industry, *internal* dimensions and certain other characteristics such as the hardness of the case heads are up to the engineers of each individual manufacturer and may vary quite widely between brands or even between lots from the same brand-name maker. Obviously, if case walls are made thicker and external dimensions are standard, the volume of the cases will be reduced, and this has its effect on powders, charges, and pressures. Similarly, up to a point, if case heads are made harder and thus able to withstand higher pressures, charges can be safely increased in a given case brand beyond a point which might be safe in another brand of equal quality.

The handloader is likely to encounter cases from many modern makers, including Winchester-Western, Remington-Peters, Federal, DWM, RWS, Sako, Norma, Browning, various U.S. military arsenals, and a host of others. To complicate the matter even more, the headstamp on a case doesn't necessarily indicate who made it since commercial ammo-loading firms frequently contract with competitors to supply formed brass. Companies like Speer, Super Vel, and Browning do not manufacture cartridge cases, and may buy from one supplier this year and another one next year, although the identifying headstamps will always be the same.

All this adds up to one fact of life for the handloader, and it is that he must sort his fired cases by headstamp and, preferably, by lot, and keep his various lots separate. If he assembles ammunition using three or four different brands of brass indiscriminately, he will surely produce widely varying pressures from shot to shot (which wrecks accuracy) and he may, in extreme cases, even encounter dangerous pressures.

Some reloaders have gone to the trouble to sort cases, even within a given headstamp, by weighing or by measuring volumetric differences, but the benefits derived from such painstaking efforts are simply not worth the trouble, even for super-precise benchrest competition. It may be worth doing just to convince yourself that significant differences in

Sorting brass by brand and, if possible, by lot is the first step in case preparation. Mixed batches (this one has seven different brands) are a cinch to impair accuracy and conceivably can be dangerous, because internal capacities vary widely between types.

case volume do exist, but we have another and much simpler means of achieving the same practical ends, and that is merely to purchase cases, whether as virgin brass or as factory-loaded ammo, in fairly large lots, at least 40 to 60 at a time, and to keep those lots separate. I prefer to purchase cases 100 at a time.

It's possible to mark all the cases in one lot so that they can forever be identified, by means of filing tiny nicks in the rim with a small three-cornered file. Some sort of simple system can be devised, such as one notch for one lot and two or three notches for other lots, or by filing the notches opposite certain letters or numbers in the headstamp. Be sure to make permanent notations of your code, however, because it's easy to lose track when you begin working with several different calibers. As long as the notch-filing isn't overdone, such marking in no way weakens or damages the cases.

Or one can simply keep each lot of brass in its own bin or box; that's the lazy man's way, which is to say, *my* way. However you decide to do it, *do* it; it's important.

It's also important to keep brass sorted according to the number of times it has been fired. Properly loaded, cartridge cases have a long life, but that life is not indefinite, and a few cases will be lost along the way. If you load for the hunting field, you'll probably wish to use only brass which has been fired at least once but not more than about three times, for reasons which will be discussed in another chapter. On the other hand, brass which has been fired many times, from ten to twenty or more, depending upon the specific cartridge, is best set aside for use only in low-pressure loadings for plinking or small game.

Cases which fall between these two extremes are suitable for general practice shooting, noncompetitive target shooting, and experimenting. It should become apparent, from all this, that the times-fired statistic on a lot of cases is important. For this reason, I like to load all cases in a lot, or in an identifiable sub-lot, each time I load any of them, to avoid having to keep track of some which happen to have been through the rifle's chamber five times and others which have been fired only twice. If loading in such quantities isn't practical for one reason or another, I break the lot down to sub-lots and keep them separate as well. All this sounds complicated, but it really isn't much trouble once you establish some kind of system. Perhaps this discussion will at least serve to emphasize the importance of sorting brass. It's the vital first step in any kind of metallic reloading.

The second, and equally vital, step is inspection of the cases. Once you have selected a lot of brass for a planned load and have them set up in a loading block before you, pick up each and every one of them and give it a quick bow-to-stern visual inspection. Check for split necks (or incipient splits), cracks in shoulders, and anything even hinting at a possible weakening in the case body about a quarter-inch ahead of the rim. This may take the form of a shiny ring or partial ring around the case, or any mark which suggests that the brass there has been stretched longitudinally. It appears most frequently in the belted magnum cases and those which have been fired in one of the older, rear-locking rifles of lever or slide-action types.

It's possible to be confused by the bright ring often left by a full-length resizing die on cases which have been fired at high pressures, especially in maximum-diameter chambers, but with a little practice you'll learn to make the differentiation. When in doubt, it's worth making a feeler of fine, strong wire with a tiny hook in one end and running it along the suspicious part of the inside of the case. If there is an incipient case-head separation, it will be revealed by a thinned ring of brass with a marked depression on the inside, in which the hook on your feeler will catch. If doubt persists—and it probably will, for a while—sacrifice a few of the suspected cases; section them with a fine-toothed hacksaw and inspect the inside visually.

While going over the case, note any obvious deformations, such as folded lips, serious dents, or cases which have been partially crushed or

This shiny "stretch-mark" on a .35 Remington case is a sure sign of internal damage to the brass. Trying to get "just one more load" out of such a case is a shortcut to disaster. Some sizing dies, however, will leave a similar shiny ring; only experience can teach the difference.

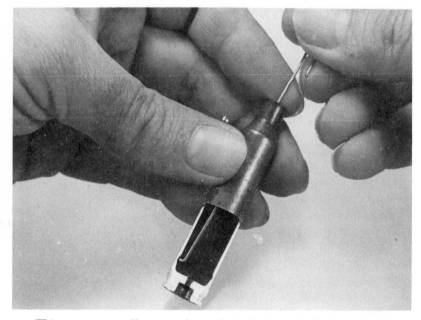

This cutaway case illustrates the method of using a hooked wire as a feeler to detect incipient head separations that are invisible from the outside of the case.

bent. If primers are still in place from the previous firing, note their condition, and especially any blackening around the primer which would indicate a gas leak. If the case has been deprimed, check for the presence of a flash-hole in the bottom of the primer pocket (yes, now and then a case comes through without one), and see that the hole is centered and appears neither oversize nor undersize. If you find not one but two flash-holes, with a small teat of brass between them, you're looking at a Berdan-primed case, which cannot be reloaded in exactly the same way as regular, Boxer-primed types. Any of these defects justifies discarding the case if it is a common caliber; in very scarce cases, some of the defects may be worth trying to correct, such as minor dents, out-of-round mouths, undersized flash-holes, etc.

If the caliber is one of the belted magnums or any of the small-bore, high-velocity cartridges and this lot of cases has been fired three to five times or more, check overall case length. The easiest way to do this is to set your micrometer dial caliber (you should have one anyway) to the maximum case-length dimension for the cartridge in question, and use it as a snap-gauge for each piece of brass. Cases tend to lengthen with re-

At left is shown a Berdan primer pocket, identifiable by the integral anvil flanked by two small flash holes. At right is a Boxer primer pocket, with no anvil and one, central, larger flash hole. All American-made cases are of the latter type, while most European cases have Berdan primers.

peated firing because brass under high temperature and pressure flows slightly. If case length is allowed to grow beyond certain limits, the case mouth can be jammed into the origin of the rifling grooves and lands upon chambering. It then cannot expand to release the bullet as gas pressures build up behind it, and those pressures can skyrocket. All major handloading manuals give maximum case length for the cartridges for which they furnish loading data, and P. O. Ackley's *Handbook for Shooters and Reloaders* gives lengths for most common and many uncommon wildcats as well. Most manuals also give what is called a "trim-to" length, which is the dimension below which cases should not be shortened. If your batch of brass proves to be overlength, you'll have to invest in a case trimmer, basically a small endmill with provision for holding the case firmly and precision adjustments for the depth of cut. The cheapest is the Lee tool, and it's a good one. More elaborate trimmers are offered by RCBS, Lyman, Redding, Forster, Bair, Bonanza, C-H, Wilson, and other firms. Pacific, RCBS, C-H, and possibly others offer file-trim dies which screw into the press like a loading die. The case is placed in the shellholder and pressed into the die, and any brass which projects above the die-top is filed away, the die being hardened to resist the file.

Some cartridges are much worse about growing than others, and some need trimming as often as every other firing, although this is rare,

Note the thinned area inside the belted-magnum case at left. A comparison with the unsectioned case at right reveals where to look for the weakened ring of brass.

but eventually almost all high-pressure cartridge cases will have to be trimmed. It's a nuisance, but it's part of the game.

Cases in a given batch of brass usually lengthen at uneven rates, so that some of the lot will be too long while the rest will be normal, or somewhere in between. If the handload you plan to assemble in those cases requires crimping, as in rifles with tubular magazines or some of the magnum revolver rounds, you'll have to trim them all to a uniform length in order to assure a uniform crimp. On the other hand, cases which headspace on the mouth must never be trimmed below standard length, for to do so would create excess headspace.

Whenever cartridge cases have been trimmed, their mouths must be deburred and chamfered. This is also true of new cases, whether virgin or the products of firing factory loads. The necessary tool is a simple and inexpensive little gimmick offered by most makers of reloading tools, or it can be the blade of an old pocketknife. The purpose is to remove the burr around the outside of the case mouth, and to chamfer lightly the inside to facilitate the starting of a bullet. The purpose is *not* to make a cookie cutter of the case mouth; if deburring and chamfering are overdone, the mouth is weakened and splitting is encouraged, especially in cases which are usually crimped onto the bullet. Deburring and chamfering need not be done at every reloading, but only on new cases and after trimming.

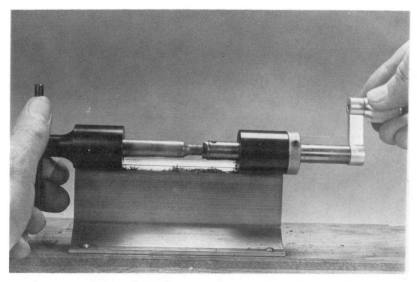

Cases must be trimmed occasionally to keep them from outgrowing maximum permissible overall-length dimensions, especially when heavy loads are used.

This equipment permits the swaging of crimped primer pockets in military cases for normal reloading procedures.

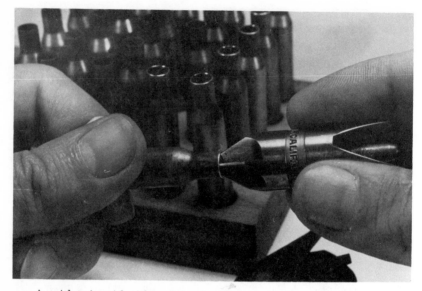

A quick twist with either of the chamfering tools shown here chamfers case mouths; reverse the tool and another twist deburrs the outside rim of the mouth.

Something should be said here about cleaning cases. I remember a jovial character who shot at my rifle club range every Saturday morning. He kept a pad of 00000-grade steel wool on his shooting bench, and whenever he wasn't firing—when targets were being changed or he was chewing the fat with another member—he was methodically polishing his rifle cases. We were amused to note that his groups were never much to brag about, but he had the shiniest cases in town!

Which says something about the relationship between clean brass and good performance: There ain't any! However, if shiny cases appeal to you, there are several ways—other than superfine steel wool—in which you can go about cleaning them. By far the best is the use of a case tumbler or vibrator, using ground nutshells, corncobs, or plastic as a polishing medium (usually with a chemical polishing agent). Such equipment is fairly expensive and takes several hours to do its job, but it will polish a large batch of brass at once and cleans both the inside and outside of the cases, plus primer pockets. It is, in fact, the only safe way I know to clean the insides of cases. Avoid chemical cleaners of the sort which require dipping or soaking the cases. If these are strong enough to really do the job, they may damage the brass, and I know of none which can eradicate the hardened powder residue which blackens the insides of fired cases. Of course, any of the various kitchen-type brass cleaners, such as Brasso, will polish the outsides of the cases, but they require time and elbow grease better reserved for actual loading, and, as I said, shiny brass shoots no better than dull brass. It should be added that *corroded* brass, with a green residue over a pitted surface, should be discarded; we're talking about the dulling and darkening which accompanies normal handling and firing, not actual chemical destruction of the metal by acids, salt water, or other agents to which cartridges are rarely exposed.

In the long run, a tumbler-type cleaner (such as used by rockhounds for polishing mineral samples) is the best bet for restoring that virgin shine to brass, and a tumbler or vibrator actually accomplishes one worthwhile object, and that is the cleaning (more or less) of the primer pockets.

At center here is one of several simple primer-pocket-cleaning tools currently on the market, flanked by a uncleaned (left) primer pocket and a clean one, ready for reloading.

This is another job which needn't be done after every firing, unless you're a perfectionist, but it should be done often enough to keep the residue which forms in the bottom of the pocket from building up enough to interfere with proper seating of the primers. This means about every second or third firing, in typical cases. It can be done with the blade of a small screwdriver, although several simple, inexpensive tools are available which do it better, faster, and easier. Primer residue is fairly brittle and easily removed, but some care should be taken to avoid enlarging the primer pocket by removal of brass, especially around the walls of the pocket.

While we're on this subject of primer pockets, it's appropriate to point out that military brass (one of the great boons to reloading in such calibers as .223 Remington, .308, .30-06, .45 ACP, and others) requires special processing, because military primers are actually crimped into place. Depriming such once-fired cases is best done with a drift punch just small enough to pass through the flash-hole and a hammer, although some die manufacturers offer specially beefed-up decapping pins. In any case, getting spent military primers out of their pockets is a tough job, and seating fresh primers is all but impossible unless the pockets are modified. This can be accomplished by reaming or swaging. Special tools are available, or the job can be done, with proper care, with a sharp knife, trimming away the lip of brass which held the military primer in place. Great care should be exercised to avoid enlarging the pocket itself, with either the knife or a commercially made reamer. Swaging is considerably the best bet for this work, and, again, several different tools can be purchased for the job. Some are used with a loading press (RCBS) and others with a vise and a hammer (C-H and others), the chief differences being cost and convenience. This is another task which needs to be done only once, before the military case is handloaded for the first time.

You now have a batch of cases in your loading block, sorted, inspected, cleaned, trimmed, deburred, chamfered, and with primer pockets cleaned. Now, and only now, can you begin processing the brass for actual reloading. Of course, since fired primers must be removed for primer pocket inspection and cleaning, and since in most rifle cases depriming is combined with the resizing process, we have necessarily gotten a little ahead of ourselves in this discussion. Let's go back and discuss that resizing-depriming step.

I said that clean cases don't shoot any better, but I must add that dirty cases—very dirty ones, with gritty gunk attached—may damage sizing dies, causing scratches which will then be reproduced on every case sized in that die. Cases need not be shiny, but should be wiped clean before sizing. This wiping should not be with a cloth used to apply lubricant, since the grit is then merely distributed throughout the batch of cases.

In fact, anything except the fingers which is used for lubricating cases is likely to spread grit, including the inking pads so popular for lubrication. Also, nothing offers the reloader so certain a means of controlling lubrication as his fingers, and they are the instrument I prefer for applying sizing lube.

Most manufacturers of dies also sell lubricants, since proper lubrication is absolutely essential in sizing, especially full-length sizing. Making sure their customers have good lubes available saves the diemakers the profitless trouble of removing even more stuck cases than they have to as it is. All lubes sold especially for resizing work well enough, but the two I like best are sold by Hornady-Pacific and Hodgdon. These have about the consistency and feel of cold cream (but don't try cold cream as a substitute!). They wipe on and off easily, and the red Hodgdon goop actually seems to clean cases to some extent as it lubricates.

Two of several methods of lubricating cases are shown here, a greased stamp pad in the background and the greasy-fingers technique in the foreground. Either is satisfactory.

The right amount of sizing lube is important; too much produces dents in case shoulders, and too little leads to stuck cases. It's probably beneficial (and inevitable) for a new reloader to stick at least one case in a sizing die early in his career, if only to convince him of the desirability of avoiding that minor catastrophe forever afterward. When you do stick one, either buy a good stuck-case extractor and read the directions carefully before proceeding, or return the die to the manufacturer. Any other course of action will fail to remove the case and quite likely will result in a ruined sizing die.

Sizing lube must be applied very sparingly. The lubricated case should feel just slightly greasy, without a visible buildup of lubricant. The simplest method of application is to dip the tip of a forefinger in the lube and spread it over the thumb and fingers, then handle the cases thoroughly. It is not necessary to lubricate the case neck or shoulder nor, of course, the area around the extractor groove or belt since that portion of the case doesn't enter the die. Don't fret about getting your fingers greasy by this method; they'll get greasy anyhow, from handling the cases, no matter how the lube is applied.

After sizing, the lubricant must be removed from the cases. Most authorities recommend thorough wiping with a soft cloth, but I have never quite satisfied myself with merely wiping dry. Remember that the brass case must expand and cling to the walls of the chamber during the peak pressure period in firing. Too much lubricant, either on the cases or in the chamber, inhibits this action to some degree, and produces an abnormal strain upon the gun's locking system. In fact, the thrust applied upon a test gun's bolt by firing a deliberately oiled cartridge was once measured in ballistics laboratories, before the introduction of more sophisticated equipment, as a means of determining total chamber pressure.

Therefore, my own habit is to remove the lubricant from each sized case with a solvent on a paper towel. Anything will do—lighter fluid, cleaning fluid, automotive solvent. Gasoline is much too dangerous for cuse around a reloading bench, and even the naphtha-based solvents mentioned above should be used with care. Plain old lighter fluid has the advantage of being packaged in small quantities with safe closures and convenient applicator spouts. Cleaned cases should feel bone-dry, "squeaky clean," to the touch.

At this point, the hard work in reloading has been done. What remains—priming, charging, and bullet seating—goes very quickly. For this reason, a handy habit to get into, when you have no other work to do at the bench, is to preprocess cases. When you're in a hurry, or it's the night before you leave on the annual deer-hunting trip, it's a boon to be able to pick up a block full of cases ready to be primed and loaded. I try to keep every empty case I own processed and ready for loading at all times; I don't accomplish it, but I try.

Priming is the next step, and it deserves a full chapter unto itself.

In the meantime, one more occasional operation on cases belongs here, and it is annealing. You'll recall the brief discussion in the previous chapter on the microstructure of brass which can be changed by cold-working. Resizing a case cold-works it, as does bullet seating and crimping. With each reloading, therefore, the crystalline structure of the case neck and, to a lesser degree, the body is changed. The crystals of the alloy grow larger and the brass becomes harder and more brittle. This is probably the major cause of brass failure, via split necks, and it is accelerated when the rifle's chamber is too large, relatively, for the specific resizing die so that the brass is cold-worked excessively with each processing. This doesn't mean that either chamber or die is outside specifications, but, manufacturing tolerances being what they are, it happens now and then. Drastic case reforming, such as necking up or down more than one caliber, also contributes to early brass loss through hardening.

The answer is reannealing the neck and shoulder portion of the case. This reduces crystalline size and produces brass sections which are tough and springy instead of hard and brittle. However, the annealing must not be allowed to extend to the head area of the case; that portion must be left hard. The problem, then, is the application of just the right amount of heat to just the right portion of the case for just the right duration. It sounds pretty formidable, but there are ways to do it.

The one most often recommended is as follows: stand cases on their bases in a shallow tray or pie tin containing from ½ to ¾ inch of water, and heat the necks with a propane torch. As each one reaches the correct temperature, tip it over to quench in the water. This method requires a certain amount of practice in judging just when the correct temperature is reached. Some sources have said to heat the necks red hot. Don't do it. Especially on small cases, this will result in overannealed and ruined cases. The first visible color change will be to a brownish tinge, and then to a bluish one. With the torch flame applied to the mouth of the case, the color change will occur within a few seconds, and will spread to the shoulder. By this time the mouth will show the blue color shift, but as soon as the brownish tint has reached the junction of shoulder and body, the anneal is complete. Ideally, the case should be rotated during application of the flame for an even anneal.

If a large number of cases are annealed in the same pan of water, the water will rather quickly become almost hot enough to boil, and should be exchanged for cold water. Ordinary tap water is cold enough.

A more satisfactory method of annealing is available if you happen to have access to an electric lead melting pot such as is used in casting bullets. Fill the pot with lead, melt and flux it (see fluxing instructions in the chapter on casting), and set the pot's thermostat at 750° to 800° Fahrenheit. Provide yourself with a handy vial of light machine oil, and a bucket of water. Pick up each case by the head, mouth down, and dip it into the oil for about half its length. Shake off the excess oil and dip the neck, shoulder, and about a quarter-inch of the body into the hot lead. Just as you begin to feel an uncomfortable degree of heat in your fingertips, drop the case into the water.

The advantage of this method of annealing is that you know the temperature being applied (assuming the pot thermostat is reasonably accurate), and you cannot stand enough heat to permit overannealing. Even so, it's hot work and something you won't want to do more often than necessary.

If a large batch of cases is to be annealed, a little ingenuity will produce some sort of device for holding up to a dozen cases in the lead at

Another method of annealing cases involves standing them in water, heating the necks with a propane torch, and tipping them over to quench. This is most suitable for small lots.

once, with a quick-release feature so they can be quenched before too much heat spreads to the head sections. With such a device, of course, you lose your built-in heat control and must anneal by time rather than feel. About 8 to 12 seconds (not more than 15 seconds, in any case) will be about right.

The annealed cases will then need to be washed thoroughly in a grease-cutting detergent to remove the oil, and dried before loading. Drying proceeds more rapidly if the cases have been deprimed (and then there's no chance of accidentally mixing a live primer in with spent ones). For small batches, a lady's hairdryer speeds up the process. For larger quantities, the cases can be spread on a cookie sheet and dried in the oven, provided you're quite confident of your oven's temperature controls, and you don't set the controls higher than 200°. One-fifty is safer, but slower. If compressed air is available, the best solution is blowing out the water and air-drying.

Essentially, the annealing process involves applying at least 750° but not more than 950° to the neck-shoulder portion of the case, without allowing the head portion to reach a temperature higher than about 200°.

The molten-lead technique of annealing cases. Brass is dipped in light oil, immersed in lead to juncture of shoulder and body, and then dropped into cold water. Bare fingers insure against getting the case head too hot.

More space has probably been spent on annealing than the average reloader will find it's worth, since the process is required only under special conditions. When it is required, however, nothing else will serve. The description of annealing has been included here for the sake of completeness, and not to scare off a would-be handloader. Many reload for twenty years without ever annealing a cartridge case.

6

Primers and Priming

There's an enormous amount of precision, reliability, and power packed into small-arms primers, tiny as they are. The longer you handload, the more respect you'll develop for primer manufacturers, but somewhere along the line you'll probably cuss them a few times, too. When a round of reloaded ammunition fails to fire, the first explanation which springs to mind is a defective primer. Such things exist; in my decades at the loading bench I've seen one primer without a pellet of detonating compound, and several more which lacked anvils, out of close to a quarter-million examined. However, I've never had a misfire which I could positively pin on a defective primer. There are so many other factors in the gun, the reloader's technique, and the loading tools which can create firing malfunctions that I'd estimate the odds on a primer misfire at less than one in a thousand. In this chapter, we'll take a hard look at how to eliminate as many of those other factors as possible, so that when you do have a misfire, you may be able to gripe to the manufacturer of the primer.

A rifle or pistol primer has three components: the cup, the pellet of priming compound, and the anvil (for Boxer primers; Berdan types will come later). All three are important to proper functioning. The cup must be of correct diameter to fit snugly in the pocket of the case, the correct

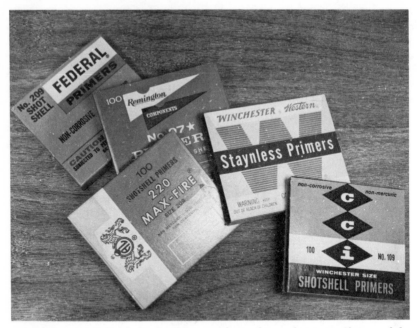

All brands of shotshell primers currently on the market are uniform and dependable in proper loads, but they are not necessarily interchangeable (even though of the same size) in a given loading formula. Always use the primer called for in the load specifications.

thickness to contain chamber pressures even when dented by the blow of the firing pin, and the correct hardness to accept a full-depth indentation. The pellet must be of the correct chemical composition for sensitivity and of the correct weight to produce enough flame to ignite the powder. The anvil must be of correct design to seat properly and straight and to support the blow of the firing pin.

When the firing pin indents the primer cup, it pinches the pellet between it and the anvil, detonating the compound. A very fine balance is necessary in the compound for just enough sensitivity but not too much, for the sake of safe handling. Never underestimate the potency of priming compounds. Some years ago, I'm told, a workman at a primer manufacturing facility was carrying a bucket of loose primers, an act which would never be tolerated under modern practices. Apparently dust from the pellets sifted down to the bottom of the bucket and the whole bucket detonated. The report I had was that they never found any part of the workman except his shoes.

The anvil of a Boxer primer should be pressed deeper into the cup, stressing the pellet of priming compound, when the primer is seated. This is why the anvil feet protrude as shown at left.

An acquaintance of mine had a quantity of rifle primers he estimates at about a hundred detonate in a plastic medicine vial in his left hand. He lost his hand and the sight in his left eye, and underwent a series of operations for cosmetic repairs to his face, arm, and upper body, suffering a great deal of pain, a staggering financial setback, and the loss of a part of his livelihood. He was a gunsmith.

Such tragedies serve to illustrate the inherent explosive power of small-arms primers, but they can be avoided totally by understanding and adhering to a few simple precautions. The first is *never* store primers in

The wrong way and the right way to store primers. *Never* keep loose primers in any sort of container, as at left; *always* store them in the sleeved trays in which they were originally packed at the factory.

any kind of container other than the original factory packaging. The second is to go back and reread that last sentence several times. If you find it desirable to decap live primers and intend to save them for future reuse, save a few empty factory primer trays in which to store them. Do not keep live primers, however few, loose in any sort of miscellaneous container, and most especially not one made of glass, such as a jelly jar.

Never have more loose primers on your loading bench than you have cases to prime at that moment. Obviously, it's folly to subject primers to heat, impact, or electrical current.

If these few rules are religiously observed, small-arms primers are no more dangerous than so many BBs; if they had been observed, neither of the two incidents described above, or the many others I've heard of, would have occurred.

With these warnings out of the way, we can proceed to the right ways to employ primers. They are the sparkplugs which make our handloads go; without them there would be no such hobby as reloading.

The principal ingredient in all modern primers, regardless of manufacturer, is lead styphnate. Lead styphnate replaced two earlier compounds, mercury fulminate and potassium chlorate, in all commercial ammunition and in primers furnished for reloading shortly after 1930. This was necessary because the mercury fulminate, upon firing, produced compounds which made the brass case brittle and destroyed it for further use, and the potassium chlorate deposited compounds in the rifle's bore which guaranteed almost instant rust unless immediate and special cleaning procedures were followed after firing. Primers containing these two chemicals are called "mercuric, corrosive."

The significance of all this to the reloader lies in the possibility of old lots of ammunition turning up carrying such primers. The use of mercuric, corrosive primers in certain batches of military ammunition continued until at least 1954, and they may be found in military .30-06, .45 ACP, and 7.62 NATO (.308) cartridges. Caliber .30 M-1 Carbine ammo was never loaded with corrosive primers. Civilian sporting ammunition loaded prior to about 1927 may be assumed to have mercuric, corrosive, or both types of primers. All commercial ammunition having nonmercuric, noncorrosive primers, and all such primers sold for reloading, carry statements to that effect on the factory packaging. Except for a few lots of military ammo which can be identified by headstamp, however, there is no way to be certain whether old ammo or primers which are loose or which have been repackaged are corrosive or noncorrosive.

Since cases in many of the old-time calibers are quite scarce and expensive, a handloader who discovers a supply of primed cases or loaded ammo for his old buffalo-buster faces a dilemma. If he fires the cartridges and they happen to be loaded with mercuric primers, he has ruined the cases. No known treatment after firing can restore mercury-damaged brass to service. If he is aware of the possibility of chlorate corrosion, he can protect the gun after firing by prompt and thorough cleaning with hot soapy water and a military-style bore cleaner, but he may have destroyed his precious hoard of brass for reloading.

It's best to take no chances. The bullets should be pulled and saved and the powder charges discarded. Then squirt a shot of a lubricant known as WD-40 into the mouth of each case. This stuff is the best primer-killer I know, and after a few hours, more than 99 percent of the primers will be deactivated. Now the cases can be deprimed in the usual fashion, using more than ordinary gentleness in operating the tool out of respect for that remaining less-than-one-percent which may not be quite dead. Actually, even if a primer does fire in this process, no danger to the reloader is involved, although the case may be ruined (if the primer was mercuric) and the die should be cleaned in the same manner as a gun in which corrosive primers have been fired.

The brass can now be cleaned up and reloaded in the normal manner, with modern components.

The problem is a bit more complicated with mercuric and/or corrosive military stuff with crimped-in primers. After dousing with WD-40, you can try decapping the cases with an extra-stout depriming pin in your sizing die stem. I'd have to recommend against the drift-punch-and-hammer treatment; a single live primer in the batch is one too many when the case is not enclosed in a steel die and your hands are over the mouth. Best deep-six the whole lot and start over with modern brass.

Primers for modern cases come in two sizes, large (.210" diameter) and small (.175" diameter). There are also primers made in each size specifically for rifles and pistol cartridges, the latter having a smaller pellet and thinner, softer cups to accommodate the lighter firing-pin blows and smaller powder charges of most handguns. Although they'll fit, resist the temptation to substitute rifle for pistol primers, or vice versa, when you find yourself out of stock when all the stores are closed. Serious ignition difficulties are sure to result.

There are also a number of special variations in each size and type of primer, the most familiar being the so-called "magnum" versions. These are essentially nothing more than standard primers with about 50 percent more pellet by weight. They are useful when trying to build a fire under massive charges of very slow-burning powders such as are common in the big-belted magnum cartridges, among others, or when burning certain hard-to-ignite propellants. These magnum primers may elevate chamber pressures somewhat if substituted in a load established with standard or nonmagnum primers. Follow primer specifications in published loading data. When switching from a standard to a magnum primer in an established load, it's advisable to reduce the powder charge a couple of grains for test firing. Usually, you'll find you can work the load back up to or very near the previously established powder charge without symptoms of excessive pressures, but don't take that for granted.

Another specialty primer offered by several makers is a small rifle type designed for high-pressure loads in .222 Remington-sized cases, especially including the various .17 calibers. A fairly recent innovation is the so-called "benchrest" primer, said to be manufactured to exceptionally high standards of uniformity for super-accurate bench rifles and varminters.

Shotshell primers, Berdan primers, and percussion caps are still other types which will be discussed in more detail in the appropriate places. A table of primer interchangeability and manufacturer's designations is included here to help straighten out the confusion.

Once the correct primer for the load in question is selected, all that remains is to poke it into the primer pocket, right? Wrong! Like everything else about reloading, there's more to priming than meets the eye.

Most bench-mounted metallic reloading presses come equipped with some sort of priming device, and these work well enough for all practical purposes. The mechanical advantage of such presses is so great, however, that they impart no "feel" to the operator seating primers, nor do most of them have any sort of positive stop to ensure that all primers are seated to the same depth. These facts explain the presence on the market of a couple of dozen different tools, ranging in price from about $3 to more than $30, whose sole purpose is to seat primers. Most of these utilize the same shellholders used in the presses, have gravity-feed primer magazines to speed up production, and offer a great deal of sensitivity, the importance of which we shall discuss presently.

My favorite of the lot is also the cheapest, the little thumb-pressure-operated Lee priming tool, which is so sensitive that I can actually feel the primer bottom in its pocket. More important, I can easily detect the slightest enlargement of the primer pocket.

When a handload which produces too much pressure is fired, the entire cartridge case head is swelled, and the primer pocket itself is enlarged slightly. If the same load is fired repeatedly in the same case, the pocket will continue to expand, until it becomes too large to provide a snug press fit for a fresh primer. In extreme cases, you can actually seat a primer in an expanded pocket without tools, using your thumb, and in even more

PRIMER TABLE I (Boxer)

Mfgr.	Small Rifle	Small Rifle Magnum	Large Rifle	Large Rifle Magnum	Small Pistol	Small Pistol Magnum	Large Pistol	Large Pistol Magnum
CCI	400 BR-4	450	200 BR-2	250	500	550	300	350
Remington	6½	7½	9½	9½M	1½	5½	2½	—
Winchester-Western	6½-116	—	8½-120	—	1½-108	1½-108M	7-111	7M-111F
Federal	200 205	—	210	215	100	—	150	—
Alcan (S&W)	SR	—	LR	—	SP	—	LP	—
Hodgdon	SR	—	LR	—	SP	—	LP	—
Norma	SR	—	LR	—	SP	—	LP	—
C-I-L	1½	—	8½	—	1	—	2½	—
RWS-Sinoxid	4003	—	5341	5342	4031	—	5337	—

PRIMER TABLE II (Berdan)

Mfgr.	.175	.177	.179	.199	.201	.210	.217	.238	.241	.242	.250	.251	.254
Eley-Kynoch	—	69	72A 74A	—	78	—	59 60 81	—	34	36	—	41	172
RWS-Sinoxid	—	1548	—	1680	—	—	1674 5601 5603 5608	1698	—	—	6000	—	1775
S&W-Alcan	175PB 175RB	—	—	199B	—	210B	217B	—	—	—	250B	—	1794 645B

extreme cases, the fired primer may simply fall out of its pocket when the fired case is extracted and handled. How rapidly this pocket-expanding process advances depends upon how much pressure is generated; in severe overloads, a single shot is all it takes to open up the pocket too much to seat a fresh cap. Thus, the condition of the primer pockets in fired cases is a useful indicator of the pressure levels of previous firing. A loose pocket, into which a new primer slips with suspicious ease, even in a tool of low mechanical advantage especially made for priming, is a double warning signal; it mandates the discarding of that particular case because it has obviously been overstressed, and it shouts that the previous loading(s) was

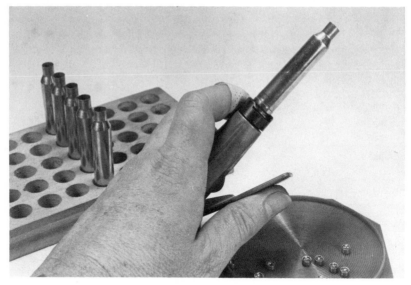

This Lee priming tool offers excellent sensitivity at a bargain price.

All modern metallic reloading presses come equipped with a priming device, most of which are similar to this swinging arm that delivers the primer through a slot in the ram and a hole through the shellholder.

Special tools for the sole purpose of priming cases, like this one by R.C.B.S., may speed up production considerably.

too hot. In truth, the feel of inserting new caps into processed cases is a part of cartridge-case inspection.

Assuming all pockets are suitably tight, the one remaining consideration is the depth to which primers are to be seated. To begin with, they must be seated at least flush, and ideally a few thousandths of an inch below flush, with the case head. A "high primer," as one is called which is not quite flush, can cause accidental discharges, especially in the slam-bang operation of semiautomatic weapons. Such discharges are termed "slam-fires," and they invariably result from high primers, if the gun itself is normal.

If you will squint carefully at a live primer in profile, preferably with a magnifying glass, you will note that the feet of the anvil legs protrude slightly from the mouth of the cup. When a primer is seated in its pocket, these feet bottom first. Slight additional pressure then forces the anvil to slide into the cup a little, prestressing the pellet of priming compound. This design is intentional, and provides for reliable and uniform functioning of the cap. If the primer is seated so that the anvil feet do not touch the bottom of the pocket, then part of the force of the firing pin must be diverted from its primary purpose of indenting the cup and used to fully seat the primer. This usually results in hang-fires or even misfires, and at best destroys uniformity of powder ignition.

On the other hand, if the primer is seated too deeply, the anvil will be forced into the cup far enough to crack or crush the pellet of detonating compound, also resulting in hang-fires and erratic ignition. In short, primers must be seated, not too deeply and not too shallowly, but just right. That's why the sensitivity of special priming tools is valuable, especially to the reloader who's a perfectionist.

Proper seating depth necessarily varies from case to case, since manufacturing tolerances produce slight variations in the depths of pockets, as well as in primers. A depth micrometer is especially made for measuring primer-seating depths, and is the ultimate in precision, but the tip of the human forefinger has more than enough sensitivity to detect, with a little practice, primers which are high or abnormally deep. A suspected high primer can be confirmed by standing the primed case base-down on a smooth surface; if the primer is flush or below flush with the case head, it will stand steadily. If the primer is high, even by a couple thousandths of an inch, it will rock. I know that sounds too simple in a deep, scientific book like this one, but it works.

One other point: If you must err in primer seating, it's best to err on the side of too deep than too high.

We now see the importance of cleaning primer pockets of the residue of previous firings. If this residue is allowed to accumulate in the bottom of the pocket, it interferes with proper seating of new primers.

A few years ago, primers were manufactured in two styles, according to the maker's taste. Some had flat-faced cups and others were rounded, and loading-tool makers were forced to furnish priming punches in both styles and, of course, in large and small sizes. Today, almost all primers are flat-faced, and only two punches are supplied. If you purchase a secondhand tool, however, it may have both styles of punches, and it pays to make certain that you're using not only the correct diameter but the proper style.

Oil or grease such as those contained in most common case lubricants are death to primers, and by far the most probable cause of a misfire in a handload is deactivation of the detonating compound in the primer pellet by such lubricants accidentally transferred from the case to the primer in handling the latter. This is yet another good reason for using a solvent to remove case lube after resizing. Most primers sold for reloading today are sealed, either with a disc of foil paper or a drop of lacquer, but, even so, the insidious oil may get through to the pellet.

The second most common cause of misfires is improper seating of the primer, which can result from careless use of the tools, as described above, or—more rarely—from incorrect dimensions in the tool, shellholder, or even the case itself.

Finally, the firearm may contribute to an occasional misfire. The firing pin may be broken or the tip damaged, the firing-pin spring may be broken or weak, or the chamber's headspace may be excessive, so that the case isn't properly supported against the firing pin's blow.

Another obvious cause can be the absence of a powder charge in the cartridge. This may seem unlikely, but don't think it can't happen to you. If you reload long enough, it almost certainly *will* happen to you. When it does, it may be useful for you to know that the sound of the primer's explosion cannot be heard if the bullet doesn't leave the case, and it will not be driven out of the case by the primer's force alone in most centerfire rifle cartridges. In some small pistol cartridges, it may be partially displaced or even driven into the forcing cone of the barrel.

In any case, it should be apparent that there are so many other factors which can cause misfires that a defective primer is almost never to blame. The precision with which these tiny titans are manufactured approaches perfection, and quality-control procedures are very severe. If you have a misfire, stop cursing the primer maker and begin to examine your equipment and techniques. This advice is not intended to protect the primer manufacturers from being maligned, but to speed you on your way to discovering the problem and correcting it.

Other commentaries will be made on primers and priming in the chapters on loading for the hunting field, loading for obsolete cartridges, and reloading safety.

7

Gunpowder

It is my contention that readers of this book will be a good deal less interested in the history of gunpowder (although it is an interesting one) or the manufacturing processes for making powder than in how to select and use propellant powders in handloading.

Nevertheless, an understanding of certain elementary technical aspects of powder is necessary to its intelligent employment. Therefore, we'll have to devote a little space here to the physical and chemical characteristics of this stuff called gunpowder which has had so momentous an impact upon the history of mankind, and which is the fuel for our handloads.

There are two basic breeds of gunpowder in use today, designated as black powder and smokeless powder. Black powder is a mechanical mixture of potassium nitrate (saltpeter), charcoal, and sulfur, and, despite the fact that it is man's oldest explosive substance, it is not only still in use but growing in vogue among shooters of muzzle-loading arms in the U.S. It was supplanted as a standard propellant in sporting cartridges in this country only in 1894.

The so-called smokeless powder which supplanted it is of greatest interest to reloaders today. All smokeless available to the handloader is basically nitrocellulose, formerly called "guncotton." Powders which have no

IMR 4198 is an example of an extruded, or "stick," powder. Although heavily graphited to improve flow in a volumetric measure, such powders are more subjected to bridging in handloaders' tools.

Smith & Wesson/Fiocchi Alcan AL-8, a slow-burning shotshell powder, is of the "flake" type, and is not graphited. Suitable for many handgun loads, such propellants must be metered carefully because their fluffiness tends to make charges vary slightly.

IMR 4759 is a perforated, short-grain stick powder especially designed to bulk up in reduced loads behind cast bullets and to ignite readily.

Norma 1010 is an extremely fast-burning powder for target loads in pistols, and appears to be in the form of tiny discs.

Hodgdon's H870 is an exceptionally slow-burning ball-type powder of surplus military origins. Although the individual spheres show some irregularity, none are flattened.

Winchester-Western 748 Ball, a medium-speed rifle propellant, has many of the individual balls flattened as a means of controlling burning rate. Like all ball-type powders, this one flows very evenly through measures.

other energy source than nitrocellulose are described as "single-based." The various duPont IMR powders are examples of single-based propellants.

Some gunpowders have nitroglycerine added to the nitrocellulose for higher energy content, and these are said to be "double-based" powders. Examples on the reloaders' market are those made by Hercules, Inc., and the full line of Winchester-Western Ball powders, among others.

There are advantages and disadvantages to both types of powder. Double-based propellants are nonhygroscopic, almost waterproof, have a higher energy content per unit of volume, and are generally easier to ignite. Single-based powders appear to be somewhat more stable chemically, and distinctly less temperamental at high pressure levels. They will not chemically attack the plastic of which most handloaders' powder measures are made, as double-based powders will.

Either type of powder may appear in the form of sticklike grains or flakes of several possible shapes. The other major type of powder has a distinctive shape as well as some distinctive properties. Individual granules appear to be tiny spheres, sometimes flattened slightly. This is called Ball powder by Winchester-Western (the word "Ball" is a trademark) and "Spherical" by the other major supplier of such powders, Hodgdon Powder Co., Inc. Ball powders are manufactured by totally different methods than the stick-type or extruded powders, but they are made of the same basic materials. All Ball-type powders, at the time of this writing, are double-based, and they share with double-based extruded powders the characteristics of waterproofness and high energy content. They are exceptionally stable, however, so much so that the shelf-life is said to be unknown, although Ball powders have existed for more than a quarter-century. Most Ball-type propellants are extremely dense, meaning that with them you can put more energy into a given case volume, and they meter through handloaders' powder measures with exceptional uniformity. They are thought to give lower rates of bore erosion in gun barrels than other powder forms, possibly because of their lower flame temperature.

Much of the spherical powder currently on the market today is quite difficult to ignite with a small-arms primer, and magnum primers are frequently recommended. The greatest drawback has been that the ball types deposit an unbelievably stubborn and unique form of fouling in gun bores, a fouling which is impossible to remove with conventional bore cleaners. Chemicals which will remove it efficiently may be dangerous to handle, and may damage gunstocks, furniture, or clothing. Ball powder of recent manufacture, however, has been much improved in both these areas, so much so that they are really not factors in its use by reloaders. The newer Ball powders are also said to produce much less muzzle flash than earlier lots, but this is a question of much more concern to the military than to sportsmen.

The shape and size of the individual granules of a gunpowder are critical to its burning characteristics. Consider a perfectly round granule of ball powder. It, like all other forms of smokeless, can be thought of as burning in layers, rather than all at once. Therefore, the exposed surface of the granule is what burns to evolve propellant gases, and the exposed surface of a round ball is greatest when first ignited and grows smaller as combustion proceeds. This shape is said to be "degressive."

Now imagine a stick of gunpowder of exactly the same mass, but with a lengthwise hole through it to make it into a tiny cylinder. The outside surface is ignited at the same instant that the inside surface, in the hole, begins to burn. The outer surface grows smaller as it burns, but the inner surface is growing larger at the same rate, so that the total exposed burning surface remains about the same in size until the granule is almost consumed. By adjusting the size of the hole (or the number of holes) it's even possible to make the surface *increase* in area as burning proceeds. Such configurations are called "progressive."

Further control is achieved through various chemical coatings applied to the powder granules called deterrents which tend to delay the spread of combustion across the surfaces of the powder.

All these efforts to control the rate at which the propellant, in solid form, yields up its latent energy suggest that there is something very important about that rate to the handloader, and there is. The reason that there are some sixty or so canistered powders on the handloaders' market today is that different applications require different degrees of what is called "relative quickness." The relative quickness of a powder is the single most critical property that powder possesses, from the handloader's viewpoint. He will read, in this book among other places, of "slow-burning" or "fast-burning" powders, and he may even see the phrase "burning rate." He will learn that, in general terms, big cases require slower-burning powders, that pistols and shotguns use quicker ones, and that heavy bullets call for slower powders if all else is equal. Relative quickness is the concept which will permit him to relate various powders to each other and to their designed purposes in his home-brewed ammunition. It will help him understand that, say, 50 grains of a slow-burning powder may be the perfect charge in a given cartridge, while 50 grains of a much faster powder is certain to blow his gun to bits, even though it's composed of the same stuff. The difference is the *rate* at which the energy is released.

Several tables are included here which show the different manufacturers' powders on relative-quickness scales, but it must be understood that each manufacturer has his own system, and that the RQ numbers *cannot* be used to relate Hercules powders to Winchester-Western powders. Charts have been attempted which were supposed to rank all powders from all manufacturers in order of relative quickness, and some of them have been reasonably useful, but they were not *quantitative*; in other words, they could show that H380 is faster-burning than IMR 4350, but they could not show *how much* faster. Thus, any attempt to interpolate charges from RQ tables is dangerous, especially between different brands of propellants. Mark this well: No two brands of powder on the market today are exactly alike, and direct substitutions of the same charge of another powder in an established loading are *not* permissible.

In addition to the reasons already given to support that warning, there are others. One is that a given powder is designed to perform within a given pressure range. Within that range, each additional grain-weight of powder added to the charge will produce approximately the same increment of velocity. This linear relationship disappears, however, when pressures rise above those considered normal for the powder; then pressure may rise much more swiftly than charge weight, while velocities may increase little, if any. Any increase in powder charge beyond that point is an overload.

Different types of powder respond quite differently to these factors. Extruded and ball types of approximately similar burning rates may react so differently that the ball may appear to be slower than the stick powder at certain pressure levels and much faster at higher levels. Furthermore, different case shapes may influence the burning rate; it may be "slower" in a straight-sided case than it seems to be in a bottle-necked one. The handloader need not know much about the size of such shifts for he will not have to deal with them quantitatively; what matters is that he realize that they can occur. The knowledge can help keep him out of the kind of troubles which generally follow random experiments in propellant substitution.

The designations or trade names gunpowder makers apply to their products for the handloader are just that, trade names, even though most of them are numbers. Even within a single brand line, the numbers have no definite relationship to relative quickness, application, or any other performance characteristic.

The term "canistered" is used to describe a powder which is sold at retail for reloading. Actually, it means a powder the performance parameters of which are standardized from lot to lot, so the handloader can be reasonably sure that his pet loads will not have to be redeveloped each time he opens a new canister of that particular powder. Certain popular powders, however, do reveal some changes from lot to lot, usually insignificant. Unless a load is already far too hot, the only precaution indicated when changing lots of a given powder is an extra measure of alertness while firing the first few rounds loaded out of the fresh batch.

Most manufacturers make many powders which are uncanistered, and thus not available to the public. Winchester-Western, for example, manufactures about sixty different propellants, but only eleven of these are canistered. The rest are used in loading commercial and military ammo, for which it's easier to adjust the machines to throw a slightly different charge than it is to painstakingly standardize the entire lot of powder to previous specifications.

Although a few powders have colored flakes mixed in for identification, it must be regarded as impossible to identify any gunpowder by appearance alone. To attempt to do so is to invite serious consequences. The one and only thing to be done with powder from cans with missing or illegible labels, from unlabeled containers, or from cartridges which have been unloaded, is to discard or destroy it. Make no exceptions to this policy, no matter what your buddy tells you about the origins of that coffee can full of powder. Powder costs money, and it's tempting to make

Grouped here are only a few of the more than seventy canistered gunpowders on the handloaders' market today.

a shot-in-the-dark identification to try to salvage the precious stuff; but don't do it. To do so would be little more than Russian roulette, with somewhat less drastic consequences for the loser. By the same token, when you repackage gunpowder be sure the labeling is unmistakable. If you forget to empty the reservoir of your powder measure, discard its contents unless you can be absolutely certain of the powder's identity.

If powders are accidentally mixed, flush the mixture down the toilet. I've heard of reloaders who attempted to interpolate a new burning rate for their new blend and to guess at safe loads. In most cases they plain guessed wrong.

Contrary to widely held opinion, common gunpowder is a relatively weak explosive, containing far less latent energy than ordinary gasoline or any of several other solvents and fluids frequently found around the home. With commonsense precautions, storing and handling propellant powders in the course of handloading operations present very few hazards. It's not particularly easy to set off, and when it does ignite when unconfined the result is rather unspectacular. To satisfy yourself (and/or wife, neighbors, etc.) on this point, pour about a quarter-teaspoonful of a slow-burning powder (4831, IMR 4350, N205, or the like) into a clean ashtray and light it with a kitchen match. Everyone will be thoroughly disappointed with the "fireworks." Do *not*, however, try this little demonstration with any species of black powder. It's a different and much wilder animal than smokeless, and its traits and tricks will be covered in the chapter on loading black-powder cartridges.

8

Powder Selection and Charging

As this is written, there are more than sixty canistered powders on the retail market, and probably the most perplexing question which occurs to the would-be handloader is "How do you know which powder to use in a given load?"

The answer is simple: You work from reliable, tested loading data and use the powder recommended for your bullet weight in your cartridge. If you do not exceed the maximum charge weights recommended, you will not get into trouble.

There are some general rules, however, which apply, and which you will doubtless observe for yourself in the course of studying reloading manuals. They are *very* general and are not to be relied upon in place of the aforementioned reliable loading data. Roughly, the larger the bottle-necked case you're loading, the slower-burning the powder. Straight-sided cases such as many revolver rounds, the older black-powder cartridges, and some new ones such as the .444 Marlin and .458 Winchester perform best with powders which are faster-burning than those used in bottle-necked cases of similar capacity. In a given case, the heavier the bullet being loaded, the slower-burning the powder for maximum velocity. Reduced loads in any case always require faster-burning powders than would be selected for full-power loads in the same case, regardless of bullet weight.

These rough rules of thumb apply to handgun cartridges as well as rifle cases, but within a different portion of the relative quickness scale, since even a "slow" pistol powder is faster-burning than the fastest propellants used in most centerfire rifles. Shotshell powders are also very much faster than rifle powders, but are often used in pistol cartridges and occasionally with cast bullets in very reduced loads in rifle cases.

There is not yet any system that will select powders and charges for various bullet weights and case sizes. The closest we have come to such a handy thing is the Powley Computer for Handloaders (see illustration). This slide-rule-type calculator selects powders and starting charge weights for any cartridge, even hypothetical ones, but is set up only for the duPont IMR series of propellants. It's useful but its results should always be checked against reliable reloading data before use.

Most handloaders gradually accumulate quite a variety of different powders. I try to keep most popular propellants in stock. Otherwise, the one I don't have is invariably the one I'll need when assembling an experimental series of loads late some evening when all the stores are closed.

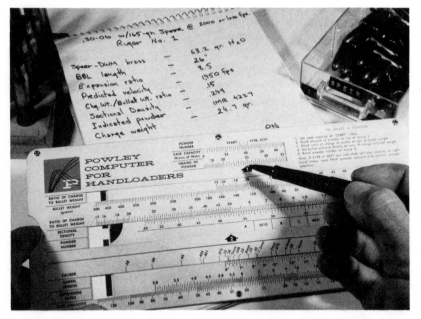

The Powley Computer for Handloaders is a cardboard slide-rule that can select powders and charge weights and predict velocities from any barrel length, and is a handy item for the reloader.

However, at today's prices, such a stock of the different powders represents quite an investment, and most readers of this book will want to know how to decide which powder to purchase to get started with a new cartridge for which they have no suitable propellants already on hand.

It must be remembered that different guns exhibit distinctive individual preferences in ammunition components, and often perform differently from other, seemingly identical guns. This is true of the test guns used in ballistics laboratories in which handloading data is developed for publication. If you acquire several different handbooks and make close comparisons between recommended powders and charges for the same cartridge, you'll discover quite a variation in the recommended maximum charges. Speer's test gun may accept several grains (weight) more of a certain powder behind a certain bullet than Hornady's—and the situation may be exactly reversed with another cartridge a few pages over. You may even find that Lyman's test gun produces highest velocities in a given combination with one powder, while in Sierra's gun an entirely different powder gives top speeds.

Handloaders today are blessed with an abundance of tested, reliable loading data from authoritative sources. It's desirable to have as many different sources as possible to permit cross-checking of maximum load recommendations, as described in the text.

These apparent contradictions do not mean that any of the data is wrong. All four of the manuals mentioned, as well as Hodgdon's, Pacific's, the NRA's, duPont's, Hercules' and others, are meticulously prepared by experts with the best modern equipment, at great expense. Contradictions mean merely that no two guns are exactly alike, and the data presented in the manual is right *for the guns used in testing.*

The odds are that your own gun will differ significantly from those used to develop the loading recommendations. This is why you'll find on every page of every reloading handbook a warning that maximum loads should be approached with caution and only after test-firing lighter charges. More about this in the chapter on working up loads.

In most cases, however, the handbooks will be in general agreement as to the best two or three powders for any bullet weight in a given cartridge, although they may rank those powders in slightly different orders. By consulting several different sources of data, you should be able to pin down which powder or two are most promising for starters. Pick the powder (or two) which appears to give near-top velocities for your cartridge and the chances are it will be most efficient in that case.

"Efficiency" can be defined in several ways. In this book the word will be used to indicate the powder which offers the highest velocity *per grain of powder.* If two powders seem to be nearly equal in this respect, the one which produces lower pressures shall be considered the more efficient. Velocity per grain of powder is easily figured from any reloading manual, and many manuals now include pressure data. If pressure units are not specified, it's a fairly safe assumption that they are CUP (copper units of pressure).

It's very useful to be able to correlate your own gun to that of the test gun used in developing loading recommendations in a handbook. This can be done only if you have access to a chronograph, but many shooting clubs and commercial ranges have such instruments these days. If you load a cartridge exactly according to recommendations, paying attention to the case types, primers, barrel lengths, and other factors specified, and discover that your rifle produces nearly the same velocity listed for that charge in the handbook, you will have a pretty fair idea that loads listed with other powders and bullet weights in that cartridge in that handbook will agree with your own results. Such information can save you a lot of time, money, and components in the future.

Even if the agreement between your own gun and the test gun is poor, you may find that the variation between them is consistent. For example, your gun may prove to accept maximum charges a couple of grains lighter or heavier than the publisher's test weapon; if such is the case, you

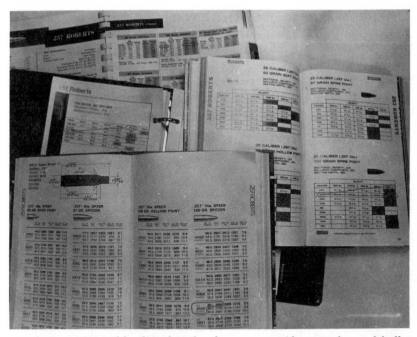

A comparison of loading data for the same cartridge, powder, and bullet weight in several different handbooks reveals differences in maximum charges and velocities. All are correct for the guns in which they were tested; perhaps none will be exactly right for your particular rifle. This is why loads must be worked up carefully.

can crank that factor into your loading plans. Don't take these correlations as gospel, however; there are other factors such as temperature, bullet seating depths, etc., which can distort them somewhat. Furthermore, a change in bullets, even to another brand of the same nominal weight and style, may make significant differences.

You will see the advice, in almost every source of reloading data you will ever read, that exceeding recommended maximum powder charges is unsafe and should never be done. For novice handloaders and those who work from a single data source this is excellent advice. But "never" is a long time, and if you work a load up to maximums in one handbook, you can almost invariably find another manual in which you have already exceeded the maximums, sometimes by a substantial margin. We will describe reliable methods of determining maximums *in your rifle* in another chapter, since they're the only maximums in which you're really interested. The point I want to make here is that "shopping" a load—that is, thumbing through several data sources in search of the hottest charge listed as safe—is poor practice. Far better to list the "max" load of a certain powder with your bullet weight from each loading manual and average the top charges, regarding that *average* as your probable maximum until proved differently. If you find, with careful testing, that your own gun will safely accept higher charges, you can continue to work upwards, but at least the averaging system will most likely keep you from getting any nasty surprises.

It is well to remember always that there is no guarantee that your particular gun will accept even the lighter charges listed in the loading tables, and that custom and wildcat rifles should be regarded with more than average suspicion until you gain some experiences with them. I once acquired a very nice custom-barreled 7×57mm Mauser rifle and set out to develop a deer load for it. Because I'm conservative, I reduced my starting powder charges a full 10 percent below listed maximums. The first shots blew the primers, a sure sign of horrendous chamber pressures, and I suspended firing operations immediately. Subsequent investigation proved that the rifle had a minimum-dimensioned chamber and that the lot of brass I was using was unusually thick-walled. I still have the rifle and enjoy reloading for it, but neither of those things might be true if my starting loads hadn't been extremely conservative. I recall another custom-barreled rifle, a .243 WCF which I got in a slick trade. At least, I thought the trade was a slick one until I found that the rifle would blow primers even with factory-loaded ammo!

Very minute differences in the dimensions of chamber, bore, and rifling can make startling differences in the maximum powder charges accepted by a firearm. The governing rule of handloading is this: Never take for granted that any gun will safely accept maximum handbook-listed charges until that fact is proved beyond doubt by actual firing.

It will have been noted by now that powder charges are always measured in terms of weight, and that the unit of weight used, at least in the U.S., is the avoirdupois *grain*. A grain is equal to 1/7000th of a pound. Some confusion is possible between a grain-*weight* of gunpowder and an individual granule, since common usage has "grain" meaning a tiny bit or piece. I shall try to keep the two words separate throughout this text, using "grain" only to indicate a unit of weight and "granule" to refer to the particle.

A powder balance or scale is essential to any but the most superficial practice of handloading ammunition. All of the powder scales on the market today are suitable to the purpose if carefully used, their chief differences being in convenience features. The typical scale is a beam balance with two counterweights, or *poises*, on the beam, and some sort of damping mechanism, most commonly magnetic. The free end of the beam has a pointer relating to a scale and there is a leveling screw in the base. Delicate, usually knife-edge, bearings permit extreme sensitivity in weighing. The scales with extra-large capacities are handy for weighing bullets and complete cartridges as well as powder charges.

The powder scale is the heart of your reloading operations, and it pays to take care of it and learn to use it correctly. First, it should be mounted at about eye level, for convenience in reading and to avoid parallax. Second, it should be kept clean and dust-free, especially in the beam bearings. Third, it should *always* be zeroed before use, even though it hasn't been moved since the last use. To do this, set both poises at zero and use the leveling screw to center the beam pointer until it is exactly on the zero mark.

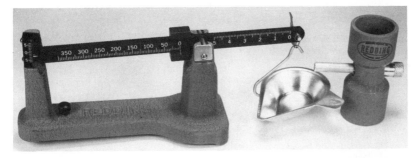

A powder scale is the indispensable tool for handloading, and the powder dripper, at right, is a great convenience for adding powder to the scale pan one kernel at a time to bring a charge weight up to exact tolerance.

Many scales have a tendency to stick slightly when the beam is in the down position. If powder is gradually added to the pan, they may stick until the weight exceeds the desired charge, at which time the beam will go "clank!" to the full-up position and you have to start over. To avoid this, tap lightly on the surface on which the scale is sitting with your knuckles (do not tap any part of the scale itself) as the pan's weight is increased. The beam will then usually come smoothly off the bottom position and proceed to balance properly. Take care with your knuckle-rapping, however, that the vibrations are not heavy enough to make the smaller poise jump a notch or two one way or the other.

Magnetically damped scales settle very quickly, usually giving one wide oscillation and one small one before coming to rest. Formerly, powder scales were damped by the motion of a paddle attached to the beam moving in a reservoir of light oil in the scale's base. I never cared for this method of damping, and prefer to use such scales without the oil. Actually, although an undamped scale takes a long time to come to rest, it really isn't any slower than a damped model if the reloader learns to read the pointer swinging rather than waiting for it to settle down. This is probably the most accurate of all methods of reading a simple balance like a powder scale, and is the method preferred by laboratory chemists for precise weighing.

An inexpensive but invaluable accessory to a powder scale is something called a powder trickler, which is a simple little gadget which is able to add powder granules to the scale pan one at a time if need be. With one of these, the reloader can use a dipper, homemade or otherwise, to drop charges into the scale pan a bit lighter than desired and rapidly bring them up to weight with the trickler. It's not as fast as a powder measure, of course, but with a little practice the difference isn't great enough to justify the cost of a measure for many handloaders.

Sooner or later, of course, you'll get a powder measure, but don't think that you will have dispensed with the need for a scale when you do.

A powder measure like this Ohaus greatly speeds production, but is not essential to handloading. Despite the numerical scales built into most measures, a good powder scale is still required for setting them.

The scale must be used to adjust the measure, which throws powder charges volumetrically, to drop the desired charge. Although some measures have micrometer adjustments which are quite accurate, you cannot be certain of returning to a specific charge weight with these adjustments alone. Always set the measure against the scale, using the micrometer adjustments on the measure merely to achieve a rough setting which can be refined with the help of the scale. Then, with the measure set just right, check every fifth or tenth charge thrown to be certain the measure locking screw hasn't loosened up. The scale is the essential final arbiter; the measure is nothing more than a convenience for high production rates. You can reload without a measure, but never without a scale.

Powder measures are peculiar beasts, with a temperament of their own. Basically simple in concept, most of them function by measuring powder which is gravity-fed from a hopper in an adjustable cavity in a rotating drum. A good measure is accurate enough for any reloading purpose, some of them capable of throwing charges consistently within plus or minus .2 grain, even with the so-called "log" powders, the large-granuled slow-burners like 4831. With smaller-grained powders, and especially with the Ball types, the accuracy you get may be even greater from charge to charge.

Such consistency, however, depends to a great extent on the operator. Handloaders with their first powder measure are usually appalled at how much the charge-to-charge variation is; then, as their proficiency increases, they discover that the tool is indeed capable of the accuracy claimed by its manufacturer. The secret is in perfect uniformity of operation. The measuring strokes of the handle should be at the same speed and the bumps at each end of the stroke made with the same force for every charge. There is a rhythm and a feel to using a powder measure which can only be gained with practice. The technique which works for me may be all wrong for you, but the key is *consistent* technique, no matter how you do it.

Especially with the long-grained powders, the measure will usually have to cut some granules as the handle is turned. Some measures are better at this than others, having sharper edges for the purpose, but all of them will hang up now and then and break your rhythm of operation. Such charges will almost always be either heavy or light. After a little time on your powder measure, you'll develop the knack of sensing these irregular charges and tossing them back into the hopper with hardly a break in the routine.

The very coarse powders will occasionally "bridge" in all measures, meaning that part or all of the charge will hang up where the drop tube narrows below the metering drum. This can be a damn nuisance, with that case receiving half a charge and the next one overflowing from a charge-and-a-half. A light tap usually breaks the bridge and allows the full charge to flow through. I know of no way to avoid this nuisance except by vigilance. Handling gunpowder demands all your attention and concentration anyhow, and this bridging business is one of the reasons.

Measures require little or no maintenance, other than not leaving double-based powders in their hoppers, even overnight. Lubrication is not recommended. Certain powders have a tendency to work their way between the drum and the hole within which it turns and can make the operation somewhat sticky. Cure this by removing the drum and cleaning the surfaces with an evaporating solvent, but do not oil.

The very simplest part of assembling a handload ought to be dumping the powder into the primed case, but even here there are some special techniques and pitfalls. Many recommended powder charges may turn out to be too bulky for the case. After checking to make certain you're using the correct charge, try pouring the charge into the case very slowly via a funnel with a long spout, perhaps four to six inches. You'll be amazed at how much more powder you can get into the case by this means, together with a little gentle tapping of the case on the bench-top to settle the charge.

One of the real hazards of handloading is the so-called double charge, which can occur with very fast-burning powders in either pistol or rifle cases. The danger exists whenever there is room in the case in question for two or more charges of the powder being loaded. If one charge is good, two are distinctly *not* better, not unless you're trying to collect on an insurance policy!

A simple means of guarding against double charges is to arrange two loading blocks, one on each side of the powder measure. In the left block are the primed cases to be charged, standing *mouth down*. Each case is picked up from this position, inverted, charged, and placed (mouth up, of course) in the other loading block. If this is made a rigid routine, double-charging a case is obviously impossible. Even so, it's an excellent practice to visually examine all charged cases under a good light before seating bullets, and checking any in which the powder level appears to be standing notably higher or lower than in the others.

Another good safety rule in reloading is never to have more than one canister of gunpowder on the bench at the same time. In this way, you'll never empty the leftover powder in your measure's hopper into the wrong can, or inadvertently dump the hopper full of the wrong powder.

Except when actually pouring powder, of course, powder canisters should be kept tightly capped at all times. Gunpowder is pretty tractable

A long-necked funnel is a godsend in getting maximum powder charges into certain cases.

stuff, but it is an extremely flammable solid, and should never be exposed to flame or embers. Reloaders who smoke at the loading bench don't have their heads screwed on right, and are asking to get them *un*screwed! Powder, like primers, should be stored in the canisters in which it comes from the factory. If you and a buddy chip in on the cost of a keg or caddy of powder and want to split it up, save a few empty canisters to receive it, and label them conspicuously. Never keep powder in glass, partly because it should be protected from light, and partly because sunlight can be focused by curved glass to actually ignite the powder. It has happened.

Powder canisters are especially designed to yield before pressures inside them rise to dangerous levels. If you place a closed canister full of powder in a fire, the container will shortly split, issuing a long, bright tongue of hissing flame, but there will be no explosion. My home burned several years ago, but none of the powder canisters in the house went up, not even those whose labels were so blackened that they were illegible. For that matter, not a primer popped (I had more than 10,000 primers and hundreds of loaded rounds of ammunition), and my loading components contributed exactly nothing to the conflagration, although damage was very extensive throughout the loading area. That story should comfort you and your insurance man when you begin to accumulate a number of different gunpowders.

Local fire regulations should be followed, of course. Mostly, they pertain to stocks of about 50 pounds of powder or more, and require storage in a powder magazine meeting certain specifications as to construction

Regular, systematic routines are important to reloading safety. On this bench surface are only the components being used at the moment, eliminating the possibility of picking up the wrong bullet or can of powder by mistake. Also, primed cases are stored mouth-down in one loading block to avoid double charging. As each is charged, it is transferred to a second block.

and heat resistance. An old refrigerator usually meets these requirements. Actually, few handloaders ever have so much powder that they become subject to such regulations.

Basically, smokeless powder in the quantities stocked by reloaders should be kept in a cool, dry, dark place in the original canisters. Naturally, a fire extinguisher should be stationed at every location where some quantity of powder is kept, including on the loading bench itself.

The shelf life of gunpowder is unlimited from a practical handloading point of view, but it can deteriorate with age. If you have some canisters of very old powders, watch for rust on the metal portions; when powder begins to break down, some of the compounds released are corrosive to ferrous metals. If you open an old can of powder and notice reddish fumes escaping, consider the powder ruined and get rid of it. In quantities of less than a cupful or so, it can simply be flushed down the toilet. In larger quantities, lay it out on a cement surface in a trail no more than 3 inches wide and light one end of it. Do not attempt to burn it in a compact pile.

Occasionally, we hear of some shop with large stocks of handloaders' components, including powder, exploding. Since it's almost impossible for smokeless to detonate under such a circumstance, such instances are always suspicious. I've investigated a few such cases, and have never heard of one in which I was convinced that the powder contributed to the explosion. Unless substantial quantities of black powder were involved, such explosions have invariably been due to leaking gas, gasoline, or some other explosive. The publicity surrounding incidents of this sort is usually pretty lurid, suggesting that possession of quantities of powder for handloading is hazardous. But anyone with a half-full can of gasoline in the garage is harboring an explosive menace dozens of times more powerful and more volatile than an equal weight of smokeless powder.

9

Bullets

A couple of years ago, I managed a rough census on the jacketed bullets available on the reloading market, and, as I remember, there were almost 900 different brands, weights, and styles; by the time you read this, there may well be many more. This suggests that, somewhere amid that staggering assortment, there should be precisely the correct bullet for any handloading job imaginable. And that's true; the trick is to find it.

Selecting the one perfect bullet for each load is by far the most crucial aspect of the game. As mentioned in the chapter on load-planning, picking the right bullet is the starting point for every handload. The reason is that the bullet is the component which does the work; the purpose of all other components is to direct the bullet to its task with suitable accuracy, velocity, and power. If the bullet fails to perform correctly, however, the load is a failure, regardless of how well case, primer, and powder did their jobs.

And when the bullet does fail to perform, nine times out of ten it's because the handloader sent the wrong bullet for the job to be done. Certain errors in selection are too obvious to require discussion: using a thin-skinned varmint bullet on big game, or a full-metal-jacketed slug on any sort of game with certain exceptions. Benchrest shooters will not be found punching their fingernail-size groups with bullets built for hunting,

Only a few of the dozens of types of bullets available to the handloader in just one caliber, .308, are shown here. They include home-cast bullets for plinking, practice, and small game, a boattailed target bullet, a low-cost "plinker" (just left of the boattail), a full-jacketed bullet for turkeys (bottom center), and hunting soft-noses in a variety of weights and shapes.

nor are long-range rifle competitors fond of short, frangible projectiles at super-high velocities. Turkey hunters can't afford such bullets, either, no matter what the velocity.

It's desirable that any bullet intended for use on game the size of whitetails and larger have a high ballistic coefficient and that it be pretty accurate, but it's absolutely essential that the bullet offer the right combination of expansion and penetration for the particular size and temperament of the game animal in question. Whitetails, mule deer, and pronghorns are light-bodied beasts succumbing readily to well-placed slugs which open up fairly quickly. Elk, moose, and other species of similar size require bullets which expand more slowly, in order to penetrate to the deep-buried vitals on these muscular, heavy-boned species. Dangerous game such as Cape buffalo, African lion, and the big American bears call for the heaviest slugs with delayed expansion characteristics. Elephants represent the extreme; they're shot with steel-jacketed "solids" which should not expand at all and which provide all the penetration which can be gotten out of a bullet of conventional construction.

Bullets for all these kinds of animals are called "game bullets," but it should be obvious that one that is right for any category mentioned here will be wrong for any of the others. A tough bullet which cannot expand properly on an animal as small as a whitetail is neither efficient nor humane, although it may kill, while a fast-opening bullet may not reach the vitals of one of the bigger beasts, inflicting a painful and possibly crippling wound.

Bullets designed for hunting animals smaller than whitetail deer are usually referred to as "varmint bullets," although the varmints may be as large and tough as coyote, bobcat, and javelina. Overexpansion is rarely a

The correct bullet for jackrabbits at long range is a cinch to be wrong for larger game.

problem on such creatures, and never a problem on such pests as jackrabbits, prairie dogs, or woodchucks. Nor is penetration a serious requirement. But these animals are often strafed from extreme rifle ranges, so accuracy, flatness of trajectory, and wind resistance are critical.

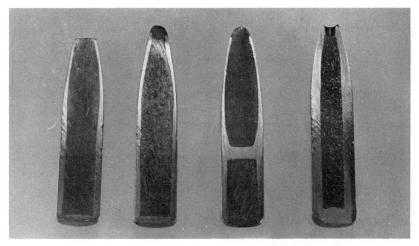

These four bullets are of identical weight and diameter, but note the major differences in internal design and construction, according to the makers' tastes.

Persons who think all bullets are alike, except for caliber, are certainly not handloaders. About a thousand different designs are available today.

Hundreds, maybe thousands, of different construction features, gimmicks, and techniques have been tried in the history of smokeless-powder bullet-making to achieve one or more of these various requirements. Many have worked, but fell by the wayside in the heat of commercial competition. If you come up with a brilliant idea for promoting expansion along with positive penetration, the chances are it's already been thought of. Everything from soldering cores into their jackets to the using of two different cores of different hardnesses or even two different metals has been tried, along with fancy jackets, metal or plastic wedges to promote expansion, protective nose-caps like the famous "Silvertip" to delay

This bullet lost its core in a big-game animal; core and jacket were recovered separately. Such recovery efforts add greatly to a handloader's knowledge of impact performance of hunting bullets.

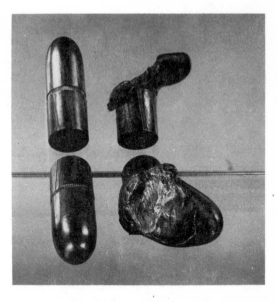

These two .458 Winchester Magnum full-jacketed bullets have both been fired into African Cape buffalo. The one at left performed perfectly and, except for the rifling marks, can hardly be distinguished from an unfired bullet. The jacket of the right-hand specimen ruptured. Such failures on dangerous game can be hazardous to the hunter. The handloader can learn a great deal from recovered game bullets.

expansion, and dozens more. Cartridge collectors sometimes specialize in all the vast variety of ignition systems that have been tried in self-contained cartridges; an even more impressive array could be assembled of trick hunting-bullet designs.

We keep coming back to the basics, a lead-alloy core enveloped in a gilding-metal jacket, with expansion controlled by hollow points, nose shape, amount of exposed lead, jacket profile, scoring of the jacket to create fracture lines, or combinations and minor variations on these themes. The result, for the handloader, is a fantastic selection of custom bullets. Most manufacturers, of course, claim that their bullets will do everything well, and such claims are doubtless sincere. But long, hard experience has proved that certain bullets work reliably on any game to which they are suited, others are remarkably accurate and efficient ballistically, and not too often do the twain meet. I know of no way for a novice handloader to learn the differences except by reading, talking to experts, and testing for himself.

This is no cop-out; it's true that I could categorize the bullets available today according to my own experience, but over the life I hope this book will have there are certain to be so many changes that my information would be completely obsolete, so much so that I'd be doing both the manufacturers and the readers a disservice. That's how dynamic and competitive the custom-bullet business has become in recent years.

I can say one thing, however: Elaborately constructed bullets, like those made by Nosler or Bitterroot and others, seem expensive by com-

These Bitterroot 7mm 175-grain bullets are among the most reliable the handloading hunter can select. Note the very thick, pure copper jacket, which is bonded to the lead core for minimum weight loss upon impact and classic mushrooming. The bullet at right was recovered from a 450-pound gemsbok bull, retaining more than 90 percent of its original mass.

parison with conventional bullets. But the cost of the bullets expended on a long-dreamed-of and expensive hunting trip is trifling at ten times the usual price. The right bullet for a demanding shot which, if successful, will climax that trip with a lifetime memory, however, would be literally worth its weight in gold at that moment.

Bullets are *not* the place to economize in hunting handloads!

Nor in target loads, for that matter. A man who competes seriously with a rifle or handgun, whether in benchrest, smallbore, National Match, or whatever kind of tournament, needs a cheap bullet—the one that is likely to cost him that last, vital point for victory—like he needs a chronic case of M-1 thumb!

Plinking and practice loads (which for most of us represent the bulk of our handloading) *are* the spot to save a buck, use up stocks of bullets which didn't pan out for the purpose you bought them, or even try making your own, either cast or swaged.

Assuming a good-quality brand name, I know of no nondestructive testing technique that can predict bullet performance. Concentricity is important, but there probably aren't three dozen men in the U.S. who can detect significant out-of-roundness with the best micrometer ever

Internal construction of a hunting bullet is crucial to expansion and penetration characteristics upon impact. At left is a 7mm 175-grain Nosler, unfired. At center is an identical bullet sectioned to reveal the partitioned jacket, while at right is another identical slug recovered from the body of an African greater kudu. Note the typical Nosler performance: loss of the front core and retention of 65 percent of original mass.

made, although there are thousands who *think* they can. It could be done, probably, with an optical comparator, but no handloader has one, and if he did he'd find the comparator slower than actual loading and firing as a method of testing. Uniform weight is important, and a batch of bullets can be sorted into weight groups with an ordinary powder scale, but improvement in grouping ability with these groups is sure to be masked by all the other multitudinous factors involved in actual firing tests. Only if the weight variation within a batch is extreme, on the order of plus-or-minus half a grain, is the result likely to be detectable on target in anything except the finest benchrest rifles. Even then, the bullet may perform beautifully on game, if that's its purpose.

Considerations of sectional density, ballistic coefficient, weight, and wind resistance have already been discussed under "Basic Ballistics." So-called brush-bucking ability will be discussed under "Loading for the Hunting Field."

All that's left is to plug the bullet into our sorted, inspected, cleaned, chamfered, deburred, primed, charged cartridge case. It's neces-

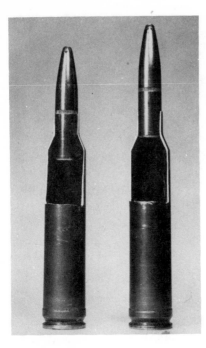

The bullet in the cutaway 7mm Remington Magnum case at left is seated to standard factory-length specifications, while that at right is seated for use in a rifle whose chamber throat has been lengthened to accept such ammunition. Note how the bullet's base in the left-hand case intrudes into the powder space in the case. This is a fault in many modern cartridge designs, including the 7mm Magnum, .243 WCF, .284 WCF, 6.5mm Remington Magnum, .300 Winchester Magnum, and .350 Remington Magnum, among others.

sary to see that the expander button in the sizing die has left the case mouth the right diameter to grip the bullet firmly; thereafter the depth to which the bullet is seated is the major consideration.

Many game bullets are cannelured, having milled grooves rolled into their jackets at the point where the mouth of the case should come to make a cartridge of standard overall length. Some bullets come with two different cannelures, for use in two different cartridges; others, especially target and varmint slugs, are uncannelured.

It may happen that "standard overall length"—that is, the overall length to which factory cartridges are loaded—doesn't suit your purposes. You want to seat the bullet deeper or shallower for one reason or another. There is no reason a bullet must be seated to any specific depth except for mechanical considerations. In a repeating rifle, for example, the space in the magazine imposes an overall-length limit on cartridges, and sometimes minor adjustments in seating depth can smooth feeding from magazine to chamber. But the major concern is the relationship of the bullet to the chamber throat when the loaded cartridge is fully chambered.

If the bullet is seated so far out that it is jammed solidly into the origin of the rifling, or "lede," serious pressure jumps may ensue because the bullet is delayed an additional fraction of second before it begins to move

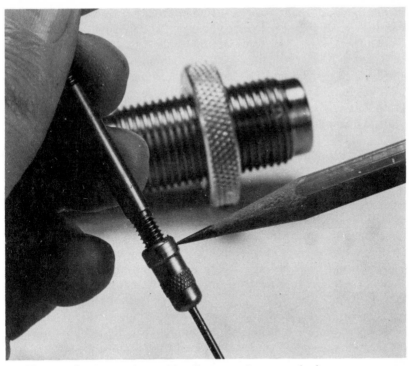

The pencil points to the working diameter of an expander button.

forward under the impetus of the expanding powder gases. It will also make the breeching system of the gun difficult to lock, perhaps slowing the vital second shot at escaping game or wrecking a target shooter's rapid-fire rhythm. Finally, if the bolt is opened without firing the round, the bullet may be held firmly enough by the rifling to be pulled out of the case, spilling powder into the action of the gun and requiring the use of a cleaning rod to remove the bullet.

On the other hand, too-deep seating can also increase pressures somewhat, by reducing the volume of the combustion chamber within the case. Except in extreme cases, the magnitude of pressure increase will rarely be disastrous, but it's certainly undesirable and unnecessary. Accuracy frequently suffers from seating bullets too deeply, however, because the bullet must jump so far from the case mouth to the rifling. During this jump, under the impulse of thousands of pounds per square inch, it is completely unsupported, and usually arrives at the lede yawing or slightly cocked. The lede may straighten it out partially, but most likely it will be driven through the bore in a position in which the bullet's center of form no longer corresponds with its center of rotation. It then leaves the muzzle in a condition of dynamic imbalance, and the result is a wild shot.

Most reloaders, therefore, seat rifle bullets to very lightly touch or barely fail to touch the lands. Benchrest shooters mostly prefer fairly firm contact between the bullet's ogive and the rifling, while hunters like a small but positive clearance. Some experimenting will be required to determine exactly how much clearance gives best results in each different rifle and loading, but a good starting point is somewhere between .030 to .060 inch.

There are a couple of ways to determine the amount of clearance. The easiest is to take a fired case and insert a bullet in the neck with the fingers. The bullet should be an easy sliding fit; if it is too loose, it may be necessary to run the case into the sizing die just enough to size a tenth of an inch off the mouth. The bullet should be seated as long as possible. Then carefully chamber the dummy round and gently close the bolt. Contact with the lands should push the bullet into the case neck, so that the resulting overall cartridge length can be measured. This round can then be used as a gauge to set the seating die to seat bullets a fraction of an inch shorter.

The other and more precise way of measuring seating depth is to make up a dummy (repeat: *dummy*) round with the bullet seated to about factory length. Chamber this round in the rifle and insert a cleaning rod down the muzzle until it comes to rest on the tip of the bullet. Mark the rod at the muzzle. Then extract the dummy round and drop a *loose* bullet point-first into the chamber with the muzzle pointed down. With a cleaning rod, tap very lightly a couple of times on the base of the bullet. Now, handling the rifle gingerly, turn it butt-down and reinsert the rod, allowing it to come to rest very lightly on the bullet's nose. The rod is again marked at the muzzle and the distance between the two marks will be the difference between the overall length of your dummy round and the longest feasible seating with that bullet in that weapon. This technique sounds complicated, but it's really rather easy and extremely accurate.

Bear in mind, though, that all these measurements are *overall* cartridge length, but it isn't the tip of the bullet which contacts the rifling (or the seating stem in the seating die, either); it's some point on the ogive, well back from the tip and just in front of the full-diameter section of the projectile. If you're ever in doubt as to whether all your measurements and calculations have produced a round which is actually touching the rifling lede, there's a very simple method of finding out. Again, make up a *dummy* round, without primer or powder, and smoke the bullet

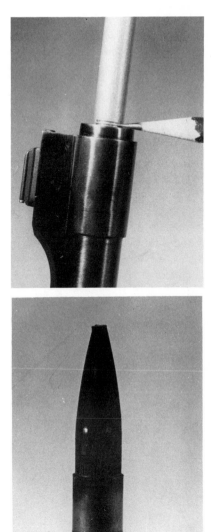

These two marks on the cleaning rod reveal the clearance between the bullet in a chambered cartridge and the origin of the rifling in the barrel, by the method described in the text.

Contact between bullet and rifling is easily detected by smoking a dummy round with a match and chambering it. Note the shiny spot where this bullet touched the lands.

sooty black in the flame of a kitchen match (away from the loading bench, of course). Then gently chamber the round and just as gently extract it. The faintest contact between bullet and lands will show clearly as bright copper spots against the velvety black soot. The only confusion may arise during extraction in rifles equipped with a plunger-type ejector mounted in the bolt-face. Such ejectors will cock the dummy round to the side as it is withdrawn from the chamber and may cause a streak of soot to be scraped off the bullet in some irregular pattern, but the land marks will still be unmistakable all around the circumference of the bullet.

Once the seating depth has been standardized for each load, you can save yourself the trouble of going through the entire process again if you'll make up another dummy round and mark it with a felt-tip pen to indicate the brand and weight of bullet. A file of such "length rounds" makes it easy to reset your seating dies to any desired load after having changed the settings.

Each different bullet to be used in a certain rifle, even those of very similar profiles, will require its own specific seating depth. Roundnosed bullets, for example, will have to be seated relatively deeper than spitzers of the same weight because their fatter ogives contact the lands sooner as the round is chambered. Unless you use only one particular bullet brand, weight, and style in a rifle, you'll be constantly changing the settings of your bullet-seating die.

Handgunners have considerably less leeway in bullet-seating than do reloaders of rifle cartridges. Nonstandard seating depths tend to jam semi-auto pistols, and revolver rounds are limited by cylinder length. There are a few exceptions, but for the most part handgun bullets are simply seated to give an overall length identical to that of factory loads, and most handgun bullets are cannelured at the correct place for crimping at this length.

A collection of dummy rounds like this vastly simplifies resetting seating dies when adjustments have been changed.

If the cannelure happens to be mislocated for your purposes, on either handgun or rifle bullets, simple canneluring tools are offered by C-H and Shooters Accessory Supply which allow you to put a cannelure on any bullet wherever you want it.

The importance of a cannelure is that the type of crimp used by most reloaders (when they use one) relies upon the presence of a cannelure. This is called a roll crimp, and most standard bullet-seating dies are provided with a shoulder in the die cavity which, when the mouth of the case is forced against it, actually rolls the case lip inward into the cannelure, locking the bullet in place. Without a cannelure, there's no place for the lip to go and the case shoulder is usually bulged, sometimes ruined.

I prefer not to crimp rifle ammunition at all unless I have to. Constant crimping and resizing as a case is reloaded repeatedly cold-works the brass at the case mouth and eventually promotes split necks. Further, there is evidence that crimping injures potential accuracy. As pointed out earlier, uniform roll-crimping demands absolutely uniform case lengths, and that means regular trimming, chamfering, and deburring.

In most cases, crimping is a waste of time in rifle loads, but there are occasions when it is essential. One of these is when the ammunition is to be used in a rifle with a tubular magazine. Consider what happens to a cartridge in such a magazine; when the rifle is fired, recoil drives it rearward but the inertia of the cartridge in the magazine causes it to tend to remain in place. This compresses the magazine follower spring which, when the rifle comes to rest at the rear of its recoil movement, drives the ammo in the magazine rearward, slamming it against the stop. Without a positive crimp, this slam-bang action may easily drive the bullet deeper into its case, which fouls up feeding and may be dangerous.

Cartridges in a box magazine or clip take a beating, too, being hurled against the front of the magazine as the rifle recoils with considerable force, more than enough to batter the soft lead of spitzer points unless the magazine is equipped with a bullet point protector. However, except in rifles of exceptionally heavy recoil, bullets subjected to such treatment will usually not be pushed back into their cases if the resizing die reduces case necks to the proper diameter to hold the bullets by friction.

Certain modern cartridges with extremely short necks simply do not have enough bearing surface gripping long, heavy bullets to hold them against heavy recoil without a crimp, and a hard one. Except in the cases of such cartridges, if you find reserve ammo coming out of the magazine after firing with bullets pushed deeper into the case than you seated them, crimping may be a temporary answer but you'll be happier locating the problem in your sizing die and correcting it.

The bullet at right has been battered by recoil in the magazine, that at left is not only battered but reseated deeper into the case by recoil forces. This dangerous occurrence can be avoided by using a smaller expander ball in the sizing die.

The other case wherein crimping is indicated is in reloading for any autoloading weapon. Cartridges are subjected to some pretty violent treatment coming out of the magazine, and uncrimped bullets may be pushed deeper in their cases when slammed against the feed-ramp as the bolt rides forward.

Many handgun cartridges for semiautomatic weapons cannot be roll-crimped because they headspace on their mouths. Several methods may be tried to keep bullets in place. First, the loaded round can be taper-crimped in a special die which squeezes the case neck more tightly around the bullet in place. No cannelure is necessary for taper-crimping. Second, the expander button in the sizing die may be dressed to a smaller diameter or removed altogether, which will necessitate great care in seating bullets to avoid crumpling case mouths. Third, you can use your canneluring tool to roll a cannelure into the *case* at the point at which the bullet's base should rest, to provide a slight shoulder inside the case to support the bullet. Fourth, you can change lots of brass; a different brand may work better. Fifth, you can change sizing dies.

Sixth, and finally, you can change pistols! Take your pick.

Revolver loads usually require heavy crimping, too, for different reasons. Heavy recoil forces work with the inertia of the bullets in uncrimped rounds to *pull* the bullets rather than to push them deeper. In such cartridges as the mighty .44 Magnum, a couple of shots may cause the bullets in the unfired cartridges to protrude so far that the cylinder cannot rotate. Even more important, with some of the slow-burning pistol powders used in the magnums, a very heavy crimp is one of the factors in uniform, complete combustion of the powder.

In general, crimping should be avoided whenever it isn't absolutely required by one of these factors. In most rifle cartridges it can be avoided; in many handgun rounds it cannot. When it cannot be avoided, there are right and wrong ways to accomplish crimping. The great majority of dies provides for crimping and bullet-seating simultaneously. This would be all right except that the geometry of the dies is such that crimping begins before the bullet is quite fully seated. With wide cannelures and the most careful adjustment of the dies, it may still work, at least well enough for casual use. But for the greatest precision and best accuracy, seating and crimping should be done in two separate steps, even though the same die is used for both purposes. In the first step, the die body is backed off a turn or two, the bullet-seating stem is adjusted to proper seating depth, and the bullets are seated.

Then the seating stem is screwed *out* a few turns so that it will not contact the seated bullets, the die body is screwed *in* to produce the desired degree of crimp, and the lot of cartridges is run through the die again. There will be a whole chapter on adjusting loading dies which will give more details on the process, but this brief description conveys the general procedure. The extra step is well worth the trouble, especially with pistol ammo, for increased uniformity and accuracy.

With the seating and crimping of the bullet, the actual process of handloading a round of ammunition is complete. Now we come to the fun part, actually firing to see how well our careful planning and labor has worked out.

10

Load Development and Testing

"Load development" might be defined as the detailed execution of the planning of a specific handload described in Chapter 3, together with the experimenting and testing necessary to assure that the load is safe, mechanically functional, and capable of its mission. In less formal handloaders' jargon, it's known as "working up a load."

That phraseology is not bad, either, since the process of developing a load literally involves beginning with powder charges well below the expected maximum weights and working, step by step, upward until the specifications for the load are achieved, or until it becomes obvious that they cannot be achieved safely with the selected components.

With the correct bullet of the job in mind, and what seems to be the most promising powder for the proposed load, the first step is to estimate the charge weight at which the desired performance is realized. Please note that I did not say "maximum performance." The word "maximum" is tossed around among reloaders and in their literature with a familiarity which is frightening, and the reason it's frightening is that very few reloaders really seem to understand what a maximum load is. The truth is that what many reloaders refer to as their "max" is actually an overload, and that they get into as little trouble as they do is a compliment to the quality and margins of safety built into modern firearms.

Let's think in terms of 10-shot series of shots, rather than of a single firing. The variables in ammunition being what they are, it's impossible that all 10 shots will register exactly the same chamber pressure and velocity. Instead, we must deal in the *average* pressure and velocity recorded over the 10-shot string. As a sidelight, the smaller the variations in such measurements, the more efficient and accurate most loads will be. In typical hunting-rifle cartridges, a difference in the pressure of the highest- and lowest-pressure shots of 1,000 PSI is quite good, and differences of as much as 10,000 PSI or even more are not at all uncommon. Such a wide variation strongly suggests that something is wrong with the load.

If you'll think about it a moment, you'll realize that it's possible for one load having only a 1,000-PSI variation to have the same average pressure for the 10-shot series as the other, showing a 10,000-PSI extreme range. Here are examples for a couple of hypothetical loads.

TEST A		TEST B	
Shot No. 1—50,400 PSI		Shot No. 1—46,800 PSI	
No. 2—51,500 PSI		No. 2—50,100 PSI	
No. 3—49,200 PSI		No. 3—51,200 PSI	
No. 4—49,700 PSI		No. 4—50,500 PSI[1]	
No. 5—50,500 PSI		No. 5—46,100 PSI	
No. 6—49,600 PSI		No. 6—59,900 PSI[2]	
No. 7—50,100 PSI		No. 7—50,400 PSI	
No. 8—49,100 PSI[1]		No. 8—46,800 PSI	
No. 9—50,000 PSI		No. 9—56,600 PSI	
No. 10—52,300 PSI[2]		No. 10—50,400 PSI	
Average	50,200 PSI	Average	50,800 PSI
Variation	3,200 PSI	Variation	13,800 PSI

[1] = lowest individual pressure
[2] = highest individual pressure
All pressures rounded to the nearest 100 PSI

Let's assume we're working with a cartridge the standard working pressure of which is 54,000 PSI. It can be seen that both these loads show an *average* pressure which is well within that limit. But note that in Test B two of the individual shots, 6 and 9, far exceeded it, one of them by a dangerous margin. Note, too, the vastly larger extreme variation for Test B, almost 14,000 PSI as opposed to only 3,200 PSI in Test A.

The hypothetical load in Test B is an overload, even though its *average* pressure is within limits. It will probably prove to be a very unsatisfactory load, too, but for the moment we're thinking only of safety. Each shot fired in a gun which exceeds the designed working pressures for that gun stresses some of its components, and those stresses are cumulative. The fact that the gun failed to blow up when the first overload was fired merely means that it's a well-made gun, but it might blow at some unexpected time in the future, not as a result of any one shot but as the result of a long series of loads which overstress its parts.

Therefore, for our purposes, an overload may be defined as any load of which the highest-pressure shot in the 10-shot series exceeds the rated limit for that cartridge. If just one shot goes over the limit, it's too hot for continued use. Thus it must be obvious that the *average* pressure for a true *maximum* handload will be well *below* the accepted pressure limits for that cartridge.

All references made in this text to maximum loadings should be interpreted in that light.

With that out of the way, let's get back to developing our load. I said that the first step is to arrive at a predicted maximum charge weight, assuming a full-power loading is planned. As described in Chapter 8, this is most easily done by consulting several different reliable data sources and taking the average of their top recommended loads for your cartridge, powder, and bullet as your projected maximum. Let's assume that the figure you arrive at as a reasonable top load is 60 grains. The procedure is to load a series of cartridges for test firing, with the initial group charged with between 5 and 10 percent less powder than you figure you'll end up with. In a familiar rifle, 5 percent is a safe figure, and amounts to a 3-grain reduction, or 57 grains for the first firings. Load three to five rounds with 57 grains, another three to five with 58 grains, and still another set with 59 grains of your selected powder. At this point, it's not a bad idea to increase charges by *half*-grain increments, especially with one of the Ball powders, or some of the extruded numbers which are known to exhibit some lot-to-lot variations in burning rate. In hot weather, or when using a fairly fast-burning powder in full charges, it's a better idea to start the half-grain steps a grain or so sooner in the series. Finally, load another five cases with 60 grains, the projected maximum.

If you're working with a rifle whose characteristics are not a known quantity, I'd suggest dropping that top charge back a full 10 percent for starters, and ascending through the last 2 grains via half-grain increases. It makes for more shooting and the expenditure of more components, but it's worth the trouble.

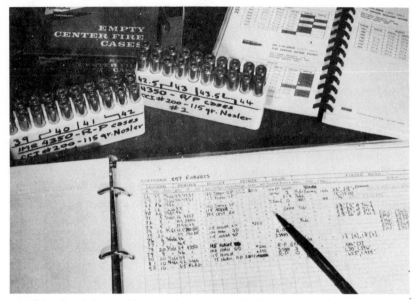

A study of the markings on the two cartridge boxes shows that these rounds constitute a pressure series, using the same powder (IMR 4350), cases (R-P), primers (CCI #200), and bullets (115-grain Nosler). In the left-hand box are five rounds each with 39, 40, 41, and 42 grains of powder, while in the right-hand box the charge-weight increments drop to a half-grain—42.5, 43, 43.5, and 44 grains. Such a gradual approach to maximum loads insures safety and may suggest where best accuracy may be found.

Now it's off to the rifle range to see if these glittering jewels you've assembled so lovingly really go BANG! when the trigger is pressed. You have loaded what is known as a pressure series, the sole purpose of which is to determine the safe maximum charge weight for that set of components *in your own rifle*. Obviously, without elaborate laboratory equipment, the individual handloader is unable to determine absolute pressure levels in his reloads. On the other hand, what he really wants to know is not the exact pressure, to the last PSI, produced by his loads, but whether those loads are safe for regular use in *his* rifle. If they are, it matters not what the numbers say; if they aren't, the numbers still don't matter.

There are quite a few indicators of high pressure, some of which require a bit of experience to interpret. They begin with the sound and feel of the rifle when it is fired. The muzzle blast of a seriously overpressure load will seem earsplitting, and the recoil will be abnormally heavy. If you're firing a familiar rifle in which enough factory ammo has been burned to give the feel of the normal blast and kick, you should notice

A drastic overload of powder wrecked this case. Fortunately, the rifle was damaged only slightly, and the shooter not at all.

immediately the increased sensations of an overload, if similar bullet weights are being used. A shooting buddy of mine once fired three overloads in his .30-06, cartridges which held a full 10 grains too much powder. Not only could he tell the difference, but *I* could tell the difference, sitting at the next bench on the firing line.

A perforated or badly leaking primer will usually produce a stinging puff of hot gases on the shooter's upper face (one of the several very good reasons to wear protective glasses at all times when shooting).

The effort required to extract the fired case is another index to high pressures. In extreme cases, even a bolt-action rifle with its powerful primary extraction can be locked up solidly, so that the bolt cannot be lifted by hand. Lever, auto, slide, and single-shot actions usually have less extraction power, and may be locked up at much lower pressures than a bolt action. In any kind of action, such a condition indicates a chamber pressure far beyond the boundaries of safety. When it occurs, there is a very good chance that the rifle has been damaged in some way. The locking system may be stretched or sprung, headspace will almost invariably have been increased dangerously, and the chamber and/or receiver ring may be swelled permanently. Certainly, serious permanent stresses have been imposed in the steel of the arm.

There are all degrees of extraction difficulty, however, ranging from the aforementioned locked-up bolt to a barely perceptible stickiness on the upstroke of the bolt handle. Even the latter, no matter how in-

A brightly polished area on a fired case head strongly suggests excessive pressures.

significant, means that the load just fired was an overload in your rifle, no matter what the reloading manual said.

When the case has been extracted, several parts of its anatomy may offer clues to pressure. If there is blackening around the primer, that primer leaked a little gas even if you didn't feel it on your face, and in normal cases it means the load was too hot. If the letters and numbers of the headstamp appear to be ironed out, so to speak—noticeably less deeply indented than on other cases in the same lot—it means the same thing. On rifles with plunger-type ejectors mounted in the bolt face, excessive pressure usually is revealed by a small, clear circle of brass which was extruded back into the ejector hole, forcing the spring-loaded ejector before it. This circle may be sheared off when the bolt is rotated if the extrusion was deep enough. A fellow in my rifle club once told me that he found these brightly polished ejector marks a convenient way to keep track of how many times his 7mm Magnum cases had been fired! I picked up my shooting gear and moved to a bench at the other end of the firing line.

Some rifles will mark cases in this fashion even with normal pressures, due to tiny burrs standing above the plane of the bolt face around the ejector hole. If they appear with loads you *know* are mild, suspect this condition, and polish the burrs away with a small, hard Arkansas stone.

General polishing of the case head around the primer usually means high pressure, too. This occurs because high-pressure loads tend to cling to the walls of the chamber, the brass case having expanded permanently, and to resist being turned by the rotating bolt head as the bolt is lifted. This, in varying degrees, is the explanation of locked-up bolts and of scraped-off ejector-hole marks, too.

An extreme case of a leaking primer. The dark smudges were made by gas escaping around the primer. Note that the primer itself reveals few signs of high pressure, from which we may theorize that the primer pocket was expanded too much from former high-pressure firings.

We come now to the primer itself, a controversial indicator of high pressures. It's true that there are no absolutely reliable means of deducing pressure levels from primer condition, nor of relating two fired primers of different makes to each other. But it's also true that any reloader can, with experience, learn to "read" fired primers, provided they are all of the same brand and lot, fired in the same rifle. If the firing-pin indentation is surrounded by a pronounced crater, it's a warning signal; it *may* mean that the rifle has a weak firing-pin spring or an oversized firing-pin hole in the bolt face, but, again, if you know from experience that your rifle has neither of these defects, that cratered primer in a previously untested load is a sign of high pressures. This is especially true if the primer is also excessively flattened. It should keep some of the radius between the face and the walls of the primer cup; if that's gone, the load was very hot. If it's not only gone but reversed, so that the primer has a flanged appearance when punched out of the pocket and viewed in profile, the load was even hotter.

The trick to getting useful information out of fired primers lies in using the same brand most of the time. You will gradually learn what different high-pressure levels look like in your primers, and can correlate these signs with the other pressure symptoms mentioned above to construct a quite dependable early-warning system which can alert you to near-maximum and higher loads. In fact, you should never rely on just one of these signs alone. If you find the bolt-lift heavier than usual but the case head and primer don't look too bad, don't choose arbitrarily to believe the primer and ignore the sticky bolt. Take everything into con-

The two primers at left reveal varying degrees of cratering. The next two cases have perforated primers, while the right-hand case shows a normal firing.

sideration and don't fail to heed even a single high-pressure sign, wherever it may turn up.

The most certain information on high pressures which the ordinary handloader can collect from his own fired cases in his own guns is with an accurate micrometer. A very good vernier caliper can also be used, but a "mike" is better. Either instrument requires some practice and skill to apply with reliable accuracy, but every handloader should have and know how to use a micrometer anyway, if only for his own convenience.

The method of pressure estimation to which I refer involves measurement of any permanent increase in the diameter of the cartridge case head after firing. Such measurements must be made with considerable

The three fired primers at left show varying degrees of flanging, while the right-hand specimen reveals rather mild pressures. Together with other symptoms, pronounced flanges can indicate high pressures.

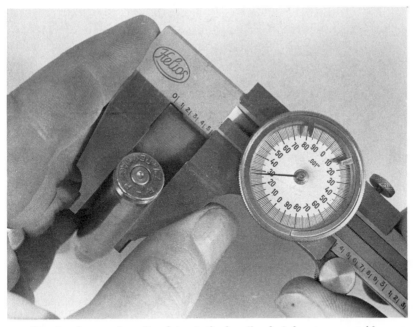

Case-head expansion after firing is the handloader's key to acceptable pressures in his reloads. Shown here is one method of measuring such expansion, on the belt of a belted magnum case. Measurements before and after firing must be taken across the same diameter to avoid mistakes due to manufacturing tolerances and out-of-round belts.

precision to be of any value, since even one half of one thousandth of an inch is significant. Several schools of thought exist as to where the measurement should be taken. On rimless cases, the head immediately forward of the extraction groove is the most popular spot, and on belted cases, the head forward of and adjacent to the belt is most favored. On rimmed cases, the head just in front of the rim is the diameter most often used. These are the locations I prefer, but some experimenters have reported good results miking the diameters of the rims or belts. With careful measurement and experience in the technique, any of these places can be used to get good information, but the values given below apply to the first ones mentioned and may or may not prove to hold true for any other places on the case head.

All cases expand noticeably in these areas on first firing, whether with factory loads or handloads, so this technique cannot be used on this firing. That first firing, however, should expand the case to match the particular chamber in which it has been fired, and any measurable further expansion on subsequent shots should be considered an indication of very high chamber pressures. In general, if the case head expands by as much as .001″; in *any* dimension, it may be considered more than ample evidence that pressures were excessive for that shot in that gun. Some authorities suggest that even .0005″ is too much, but this should certainly be regarded as the outside limit of permissible expansion. I personally prefer to keep working loads under .0001″ expansion, and recommend such a standard to the conservative handloader.

This case-head expansion, by the way, explains the loosening of primer pockets described in an earlier chapter as a high-pressure symptom.

After the expansion which takes place on the first firing, which is normal and does not necessarily indicate high chamber pressures, it's desirable that case heads retain the same dimensions indefinitely. If a load which is producing, say, .0005″ expansion is used regularly, it will produce that amount of expansion (or a little less, due to work-hardening of the brass) on each firing, so that the primer pocket will eventually loosen up and the case will be ruined for further use even though pressures are not necessarily exceeding safety limits on any individual firing.

It's important to be certain that the same diameter is being measured with the micrometer before and after firing, to reliably detect case-head expansion. Probably the very best method is to take two diameter measurements at right angles to each other and average them, but for practical purposes it's enough to take only one, provided that one is made with care. The easiest way to do this is to have notebook and pencil on the shooting bench. Before each cartridge is chambered, make a mark with a felt-tip pen on the case and take a diameter reading at that mark. Write down the measurement, preferably to four decimal places. The round is then fired, extracted, and remeasured across the same mark, and the reading is compared to the notation of the prefiring measurement. If there is no difference, no additional writing is needed. If there is some expansion, it can be noted opposite the appropriate notes for comparison. Instead of a mark on the case, you can also use one of the letters or digits on the headstamp as a marker to ensure comparable diameter measurements before and after firing. This is less precise than marking the case, but is adequate for most purposes.

Back to our series of pressure loads, charged with increasing weights of powder. As each group is fired, *all* the indices to possible high pressure discussed above should be checked. If no pressure signs appear, the next heaviest charges are fired, and so on through the series. If no symptoms of excessive pressure occur even with the expected maximum load, you may be able to take the charge up another grain or two, using the same procedures and advancing in half-grain steps. In this way, you may be able to exceed the top charge-weight recommendation in any given handbook in safety, which only means that your particular rifle is more tolerant of those maximum charges than the test guns used in compiling the handbook data.

However, if you do exceed recommended maximums, it must be done with the full realization that you're on your own, with only your own knowledge and alertness to protect you from an overload. Wherever you note high-pressure signs on cases, primers, or in the rifle's operation, even if the charge producing those signs is well *below* recommended maximums, you have arrived at or exceeded practical maximums with those components in your own rifle. When I find a load in a pressure series which produces .0005″ head expansion, I stop right there, drop back at least one grain of powder, and fire another series of ten rounds. If none of the ten reveals as much as .0005″ expansion, I call that my maximum load. If you're not all that certain of your ability to read a mike to the fourth decimal place, take .001″ as the warning signal and reduce the load giving that much expansion by at least 6 percent. If subsequent firings with that charge weight produce no significant additional expansion, primer pockets remain tight, and case life is good, you have a good, safe maximum load.

Now, if you ever substitute components in that load—change bullet, case, or primer brands or types, for example—the whole load-development procedure should be repeated. The powder charge should be reduced about two grains (in typical hunting cartridges, more in magnums) and worked back up by half-grain increments. Chances are, you'll find the old, established maximum is still safe, but maybe not, and in this game it's just as well to avoid nasty surprises. A change to a cartridge case brand averaging heavier (less internal volume) can easily reduce the max load by two grains, and tests have shown that ten different bullets of different makes but of nominally identical weights and styles in the same caliber can alter peak chamber pressures by as much as 7,000 CUP. If the load were already at maximum with the lowest-pressure bullet in this group, switching to the high-pressure one might very well shove chamber pressure off the deep end.

Such varying factors as bullet bearing length, core hardness, jacket thickness, and design are responsible for these pressure variations, and they are not predictable. We cannot say that Brand X bullets consistently require lower powder charge weights than Brand Y bullets, in all calibers and all rifles. The one and only method of making such determinations with your own equipment is by firing pressure series and measur-

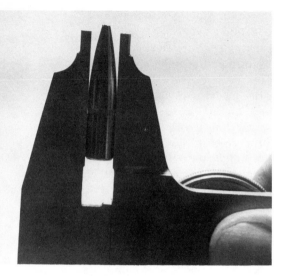

Bearing length can be compared on bullets by using the parallel jaws of a caliper to determine how much of a bullet actually contacts the bore.

ing case-head expansion. If it has begun to occur to you that, once a good, safe, accurate load has been established, the standardization of that load and all its components will save an awful lot of time and trouble, you are a very perceptive reader.

Presumably, as you fire the pressure series, you will be aiming at a target, and some indications can be gleaned from the groups made in the process of checking the pressure signs of the increasing powder charges in the series. Each charge level should be fired at a different bull's-eye and the group sizes correlated with the powder charges. It is a very broad, general rule (with many exceptions) that finest accuracy in a given cartridge will appear in loads which are somewhat below absolute maximum. I have seen some magnificent groups shot with overloads, too, but it is still not uncommon to see a linear relationship between group sizes and powder charges, when all else remains the same. We will discuss reloading specifically for best accuracy later; for the moment, we're speaking of group sizes as related to each other rather than in an absolute sense.

If you expect your maximum load to be around 60 grains of a given powder, for example, and drop back to 55 or so grains for your first pressure firings, you may see a group appear, at 100 yards of, say, 3 inches center-to-center spread between the widest bullet holes. Fifty-six grains of powder may then drop the group size to 2½ inches, 57 to 2¼ inches, 58 to 1⅞ inches, 58.5 grains of powder to 1¾ inches. Fifty-nine grains might then print a five-shot group just 1½ inches across, while another grain added to the powder charge opens the group up to 2 inches again. These numbers are selected as a hypothetical case, but they're quite representative of the results of hundreds of pressure series I've fired. It takes more than a single group to determine anything very definitive about a load's grouping potential, but such a correlation between powder charge and group size can be taken to indicate strongly that the 59-grain charge is worth further experimenting with for top accuracy, and that the load is nearing maximum levels there.

High pressures tend also to be somewhat erratic pressures, as revealed in the two tests illustrated earlier. Muzzle velocities tend to be related to pressures, and accuracy comes from uniform velocities, among other things. This is an oversimplified explanation, but it serves to show why maximum safe loads may not deliver maximum accuracy, and why reading groups shot with pressure series can add one more iota of information on handload pressures.

The final source of such information has to do with the reloading life of the cases being loaded. As a rule, the higher the pressures to which they are repeatedly subjected, the fewer shots can be gotten out of cartridge cases. The causes of failure may be manifold; necks may split, primer pockets may expand, incipient cracks may appear in case bodies. Experience with individual rifles and reloading dies is helpful in evaluating case life. With some combinations, "normal" case life may be almost indefinite, perhaps fifty shots or more. With other equipment, experience may show that about ten rounds is the normal life of a case, even at moderate pressures. As a very rough index, I expect a minimum of six to ten shots out of cases used in the high-intensity cartridges such as the 6mms and the smallbore magnums, even with top loads, and ten to twenty shots out of ordinary hunting cartridges such as the .308 and .30-06. I often get many more shots out of cases in both categories, but if cases in a certain batch begin to show a high proportion of failures before these figures are reached, I start looking for the cause. High chamber pressures are a prominent cause, although by no means the only one.

Chamber pressures and the elusive "maximum" load level are likewise a prominent source of worry and uncertainty to many handloaders, especially new ones. I hope that the message of this chapter has come across strongly. It is that absolute pressure measurement in your handloads is neither possible nor important. What is important is that you verify that *your* loads are not excessive in *your* guns, and this is easily done by the techniques described. If those loads produce good accuracy and long case life, with no head expansion of the cartridge cases, they're perfectly safe for indefinite use, no matter how many CUPs, PSI, or "quadriframmuses" of pressure they might develop. Handloads can be classified into only two categories, *safe* and *unsafe,* and the line between those categories can be reliably identified without elaborate equipment or specialized knowledge. Now that I think of it, this chapter might have been better titled "How to Stop Worrying and Learn to Love Your Handloads"!

11

Perfecting the Handload

It is axiomatic that the hottest safe load is not necessarily the best handload for any given purpose. Indeed, for many needs, a maximum load is the last thing you want, especially if you're a turkey hunter or wish to train your wife or offspring with a hunting firearm. As pointed out in Chapter 10, maximum loads are not often those giving finest accuracy.

When we think in terms of absolutes, we may lose sight of practical matters. For example, if we find in our loading manual that one powder can give a certain bullet a maximum muzzle velocity of 2,995 feet per second, and another powder is capable of 3,070 FPS, it's very easy to jump at the latter load because it's over the magic 3,000-FPS mark and appears at first glance to be so much faster than the first one. But I'll give you a written, money-back guarantee that the 75-FPS difference between these two loads (assuming they can be duplicated exactly in your rifle, which is dubious) is absolutely meaningless in actual practice. You will not be able to detect *any* difference in performance due to the difference in initial velocity under any conditions in which they are likely to be used in the field. Nor will any game animal be able to tell any difference either. For practical shooting, the two loads are identical.

It may very well come to pass, however, that the first-mentioned loading will produce significantly improved accuracy in your rifle, or show some other practical advantage which will more than offset the difference in MV. Ferreting out these possible improvements is the real fun in reloading, and I call it "perfecting" the load, at the same time admitting that, out of the thousands and thousands of handloads for rifles, pistols, and shotguns I've developed over the years, I have actually achieved perfection only once. I have only one loading, a cast-bullet load at reduced velocity for a 7×57mm Mauser rifle, which could not conceivably be improved in any way whatever. However, I'm inclined to believe that even one such perfect load in a lifetime is quite an accomplishment.

A nonshooting friend of mine once commented, upon inspecting my loading bench and listening to about two hours of enthusiastic description of the joys and inner satisfactions derived from handloading, that handloading is essentially a search for perfection. Upon long reflection, it seems to me that this noninvolved observer put his finger on an aspect of the game which I'd never heard mentioned before, hence the title of this chapter.

There are two fundamental requirements for even approaching perfection in a handload. The first is the development of a set of realistic, written specifications, described in the chapter on load planning. The second is varying only one thing at a time during the testing procedure. For example, if accuracy is a major criterion, as in a load for a long-range varmint rifle, the first step is to select a bullet known for its accuracy. If the rifle is in one of the centerfire .22 cartridges, such bullets are available from several makers, including Speer, Sierra, Nosler, Hornady, and others. Say you start with the Speer, and the brand of case and primer is pretty well determined by your current components inventory. Any of two or three powders may prove to deliver optimum accuracy, and with each powder, one particular charge weight is likely to give best results. Testing, however, should involve only one powder at a time, with the only variable the charge weights. With safe maximums already established as described in the foregoing chapter, a series of loads is assembled with charge weights varying across the range which appeared most promising for accuracy purposes. For this type of testing, not less than ten rounds of each load should be put up, to be fired in either two or three groups.

At the end of a day's shooting, you will have a very realistic idea of the charge weight which seems to deliver best accuracy with that powder. Note that during this day's shooting, the one and only variable tested was charge weight. On the next trip to the shooting range, perhaps the two most promising charge weights will be compared, shooting at least four or five five-shot groups with each. At this point, the best possible combination of that particular powder, charge weight, and bullet should become known. If the accuracy of the combination meets the previously written specifications for the load, you have arrived.

Suppose, however, that you suspect that an entirely different propellant might give even better groups. The procedure is repeated, and results compared to the earlier tests. This process can go on through the entire range of powders which are appropriate to the cartridge with which you're working, which may number from three to ten. Different rifle barrels will definitely respond to different powders differently, for reasons we cannot explain. A good load in one accurate rifle is very likely to be at least a better-than-average one in any other accurate rifle, but it may *not* be the very ultimate, perfect combination. It's worth trying several powders in trying to perfect your load; one of them may reveal a decided advantage in a given gun.

It's even more likely that your barrel will reveal a distinct preference for one particular bullet. Such preferences cannot be predicted; they must be sorted out by experimental firing. But, if bullets are what you're testing, make sure the only variable in the tests is the bullet. Using the same powder and charge weight, fire test groups of two or three different bullets (of the same weight and style, of course). One will usually turn out to hold at least a slight advantage over its competitors. I have a custom-barreled 6mm Remington which will deliver decent groups with only one bullet brand, weight, and type, but with that bullet and the powder charge which suits best, the rifle will shoot rings around most other light-weight field sporters. Without the patient testing which eventually revealed the magic combination for this rifle, I might have sold it early in the game, never knowing that it was potentially one of the most accurate rifles in my rack if only I could isolate the exact load formula it wanted. Not many guns are as stubborn and selective as this 6mm, but almost all of them will reveal similar strong preferences in components.

To repeat, the trick to isolating the one perfect combination is in varying one component at a time, while keeping everything else as nearly the same as possible. If you fire handloads featuring a couple of different bullets, two or three powders, and maybe several charge weights of each powder, you will never know, when you produce a radical improvement in grouping, which of the factors was responsible.

Speaking of factors, there are several involved in such testing of handloaders in addition to those incorporated into the ammunitions. One of the most difficult to keep consistent from test to test is the human factor—you. Interpreting test results may be difficult enough as it is, without having to wonder whether that "flyer" (wide shot outside the group) was the gun's fault, the ammo's, or yours. For this reason, most

Load testing requires a rock-solid shooting bench, a good rest, sandbags, ear protectors, and notebook. The chronograph, collimator, and spotting scope are useful time savers and data gatherers.

handloaders get to be pretty good benchrest shooters. Those who don't never really know how well their firearms can perform, and are largely guessing as to which is the best load.

The first requirement for serious group shooting is an extremely solid, stable shooting bench. Most rifle clubs have at least a few such benches for the use of their members. It is possible, although difficult, to construct a portable bench which will serve for serious load-testing. This is a book about handloading and not about carpentry; information on such projects is available from the National Rifle Association and other sources. Suffice it to say that a rest across the hood of your pickup truck, or your wife's ironing board, will *not* enable you to refine your rifle's accuracy to the utmost.

With an adequate shooting bench available, you'll need some sort of rest. This can be anything from a $60 fully adjustable shooting stand to a couple of bricks topped with a sandbag, but it must be firm and of the correct height. For years I've shot from a homemade rest constructed of a pipe nipple, floor flange, and section of channel iron which cost me about $2.50 when I built it.

Whatever sort of rest is selected, sandbags are absolutely necessary for serious testing. Probably the most common and convenient container for sand for this purpose has been the canvas bags in which lead shot for reloading shotshells is furnished. Cutoff blue-jeans legs, stitched up at each end, are also about the right dimensions. A friend of mine adds a ritzy touch to his shooting bench by using moneybags from a local bank to hold his sand. Very good leather sandbags are also available commercially.

Two sandbags are needed, one under the forearm of the rifle and the other under the toe of the buttstock. The rifle should be arranged on these supports so that the sights lie very close to the intended bull's-eye without being touched by the shooter. The rifleman is thus required to utilize the very minimum of muscular force to align the sights, which reduces at least one source of shot-to-shot variation in testing.

Every rifle displays slightly different tendencies in how it reacts to being held and fired, and some experimenting is necessary to determine the preferences of an unfamiliar piece. Some rifles do their best when held very tightly against the shoulder of the shooter, with exactly the same forces applied to the stock for every shot. Others deliver best results only when held as lightly as possible, just firmly enough to control them, and others fall between these two extremes. Hard kickers sometimes respond best to some downward forces on the forearm, but this is fairly unusual. The key factor is uniformity; however the rifle does best, do it the same for every shot. Ideally, test groups should be fired under roughly the same atmospheric conditions as those with which they are to be compared. Wind, light, and mirage can play hob with groups, and may deceive one into believing that one ammunition is more accurate than another when the reverse is actually true.

Shooting from a benchrest is not an art learned overnight, and when one is attempting to determine the absolute accuracy level of a given load or rifle, one should bear in mind that the human element can never be totally removed from the rifle/ammo/shooter equation. Indeed, it will vary from day to day and even on the same day, due to fatigue, weather, and general mood. If you doubt that, try firing a few groups when you have a headache or on a day when you had an argument with your boss.

However, groups fired on the same day with different ammunitions can reveal significant differences in performance even if you're not shooting your best that day. Negative human factors roughly cancel each other out, or are added in equal measure to all groups, so that a half-inch difference in apparent grouping potential is probably a real difference.

The question often arises as to how many shots a statistically meaningful group should contain, and how many groups must be fired to achieve a fairly high degree of certainty about our findings. Some experimenters insist that three-shot groups are valid, since three is about as many shots as are ever fired at a game animal. Others prefer the more standard five-shot group, while still others contend that nothing very useful can be learned from groups of less than ten shots. Since the object is to gain the most information from the least expenditure of components and time, the argument is by no means academic.

The answers are known, but they are contained within the rarified mysteries of the science of statistics, of which I am hardly a master. I have looked into the matter, however, and have brought out of the jungles of mathematical equations a few concepts which are serviceable to the handloader.

Generally speaking, good, solid data can be derived from five-shot groups, although it is true that ten-shoters do give a better idea of the potential of a given load—better, but not twice as good.

If decisions between two different loads are based on five consecutive five-shot groups, the chances are they will be the correct decisions almost twice as often as if based on only a single group. *Ten* five-shot groups increase the probability of a correct decision by another 60 percent or so. A professional statistician could doubtless quibble with this way of expressing the matter, but it does simplify the idea usefully.

I use five five-shot groups as my standard test. If two different ammunitions reveal a fairly large difference in average group size after five such groups of each have been measured, I assume the difference is real. If the difference is still very small after shooting five groups of each load, I load and fire five more of each, and use the average of all ten groups of each load for a comparison. At this point, I can assume that an *apparent* difference revealed by these average group sizes will be a *real* difference about 90 percent of the time. That's worth knowing, and requires no computers, sliderules, or advanced calculus.

Perfecting a load can involve many things besides accuracy, of course, but accuracy, in rifles and pistols, is a fundamental starting point. Most of the other items on our written list of specifications for a handload, such as point of impact relative to another load in the same rifle, or some specific velocity, will be dealt with in detail in other chapters. Trajectory and terminal energy can be observed or calculated while working up and accuracy-testing any handload, and such possible specifications as the use of certain powder or bullet (to use up stocks, for example) are merely a matter of decision before actual reloading begins.

In most handloaders' minds, though, "perfecting a load" centers around patient and pleasant testing with the objective of squeezing the last possible bit of performance out of a favorite rifle. There is a great sense of satisfaction to be gained from starting with a rifle which shoots 2-inch groups with factory ammunition and watching those groups shrink, perhaps to less than 1 inch, through the trial-and-error process of reloading experimenting.

12
Adjusting Loading Dies

What follows is not intended to take the place of the illustrated instructions that are furnished with reloading dies. Those instructions are, for the most part, quite thorough and particularly adapted to the design of the dies described. There are uses of such dies, however, which are not usually included in the basic instructions, because a discussion of these uses would require a small book. The die manufacturers don't write books, and I don't write elementary loading-die instructions.

Loading dies for metallic cases come in either two-die or three-die sets as a rule. Bottle-necked cartridges require only two dies, while straight-sided rounds (revolver cartridges and many of the old-time rounds) call for three-piece die sets.

In the former, resizing, depriming, and neck expanding are accomplished by a single pass through the sizing die, and the second unit seats bullets and, if desired, crimps. In three-die sets, the first die usually resizes and deprimes, the second flares case mouths, and the third seats bullets and crimps. In some brands, sizing is the only function of the first die, while the second unit deprimes and performs the flaring/expanding duty. In a few cases, a fourth die is added to the set, which does nothing but crimp case mouths onto bullets.

The older, straight-sided rifle cartridges require three-die sets, as do most handgun cartridges.

The first question the reloader faces is whether to full-length resize for every loading, or partially resize the case only. I wish I could answer that question once and for all, but I cannot. The theories are that full-length resizing overworks the brass and results in early case failure, and that partially resized cases fit the chamber in which they were fired better and offer better potential accuracy. There are some flaws in both theories. Unless the rifle's chamber is maximum and the sizing die is minimum, unlimited full-length resizing appears not to cause early case failure, after all, according to tests. It may be true that partial resizing makes for a better fit between case and chamber the second time around, but it may also make for hard chambering after two or three firings, and unless the chamber *and* die are perfectly concentric the bullet is unlikely to be held in perfect alignment with the bore unless great pains are taken to chamber the cartridge oriented exactly as it came out of that chamber after the previous firing.

Furthermore, partial resizing (or, as it is often miscalled, "neck sizing") only very frequently creates as many problems as it irons out, unless special neck-sizing-only dies are used. These are available on special order. Especially on very tapered cases such as the .257 Roberts or 7×57mm Mauser, trying to neck-size only in a full-length-sizing die often results in

The usual method of setting a die for full-length resizing is shown here, with shellholder firmly against the bottom of the die body. With both die and rifle chamber within normal tolerances, this works OK, but it may shorten cases too much in some chambers. The text gives details on adjusting die to produce ammunition that mates precisely with the rifle.

a case which cannot be chambered in the rifle, and/or one on which the headspace measurement has been altered. Hunters must full-length resize in order to achieve maximum reliability in feeding from the magazine and smooth chambering. As my years at the reloading bench lengthen, I find I tend to full-length resize everything. Accuracy in anything except benchrest rifles is as good as ever, and case life appears normal in the calibers I regularly reload.

In most cases, even if a special neck-sizing die is ordered, cases will require full-length sizing every three or four rounds anyway, if anything

So-called neck sizing in regular dies (left) is really partial resizing, as opposed to full-length sizing as shown at right. True neck-only sizing requires special dies.

approaching maximum-pressure charges is used. I suspect any difference in accuracy potential between full-length and neck-only sizing is completely submerged in the other variables, even in a very accurate field varmint rifle. Benchrest guns are in a class by themselves, usually loaded for in dies which were especially reamed to fit that particular rifle and seldom with regular bench-mounted loading presses.

The best bet for any confused handloader is to try it both ways in his dies and shoot the results in his rifle. That is, by the way, very good advice for solving most reloading problems: Go and ask your rifle!

A special problem which arises in loading for many of the modern belted magnums is early case failure via stretched or separated brass even with submaximum loads. This occurs because such cartridges headspace on their belts, and not on the case shoulder area as do rimless cases. Because head-to-shoulder length is not critical, manufacturers of rifles do not hold dimensions in the shoulder region of their chambers to very critical tolerances. When the cartridge is fired, the case shoulder is blown forward to match the chamber shoulder. Then, when the case is full-length resized for reloading, the die may set the shoulder back to factory-standard length. The whole process is repeated with each firing and reloading, but the case is steadily weakened by being stretched upon firing. Ultimately (often in as few as three firings) the case will fail via an annular crack in the brass just ahead of the heavy interior web portion. Most often, everything holds together on firing, and then the extractor jerks the head of the case out of the chamber, leaving the body in place. This can be rather embarrassing when a big bull elk is galloping out of sight over a ridge, since the rifle is out of action until some sort of rod is improvised to knock the case body out of the chamber. It could conceivably be dangerous, too, although I have not heard of a serious accident occurring thus. In any case, it's best avoided. The way to avoid it is to rest your sizing die so that the case actually headspaces on the shoulder, in the same manner as for rimless rounds, and the belt is relegated to the useless appendage it really is.

This is done by unscrewing the die body in its locking ring until it fails to touch the shoulder of a fired case. Now smoke the case shoulder with a kitchen match (I *did* say a *fired* case!), after lubricating, of course. Then run the case into the die as far as it will go, withdraw it, and examine the shoulder. The soot should be intact. Screw the die body down a half-turn and try it again. Continue this process, slowly turning the die down a little at a time until just a bare contact between the shoulder of the die cavity and that of the case develops. If this fired case will freely re-enter the rifle's chamber, you can set the lock ring at this position and

The result of standard full-length resizing of magnum (belted) cases fired in a sloppy chamber. Each firing and resizing cycle stretches the case, thinning a ring of brass just ahead of the belt, until the case separates, sometimes disastrously. This is easily avoided by adjusting sizing dies to headspace the case on the shoulder, instead of on the belt, as described in the text.

keep the die so set with the assurance that your magnum cases are not being lengthened and shortened like an accordion in the course of firing and resizing.

Experience with a given rifle may reveal that slightly more shoulder-sizing than described above is necessary for smooth chambering, especially after two or three firings. If so, screw in the die body just an eighth or a quarter turn at a time, trying the case in the rifle after each adjustment. The object is the very minimum possible sizing which will produce ammunition which feeds from the magazine into the chamber smoothly, and on which the bolt handle closes with its normal feel.

Once this point is reached, lock the die ring solidly and leave it alone. L. E. Wilson, by the way, makes a case gauge for belted magnums which has an adjustable shoulder. This is invaluable for returning your

A soot coating from a match flame reveals contact areas in a sizing die (left) and a rifle chamber (right).

sizing die to its previous setting in case you need to change it, as to resize a batch of brass not fired in your own rifle. With the Wilson gauge, the painstaking process described above is shortened to a few minutes and accuracy of resetting the die is perfect.

In the prior discussion of bullet seating, I suggested that the reloader make up a dummy round for each of his standard loads, mark on it the brand and style of bullet, and file it away. As I said there, each different bullet weight, profile, and brand will require a different seating depth. You can merely measure the overall length of each standard load and keep it in your reloading records. The bullet-seating die can then be adjusted by trial and error to produce a cartridge of correct overall length, but this takes time, is trouble, and wastes a few bullets and cases. The easy way to return to the right setting is as follows.

Screw the bullet-seating stem upward in your seating die at least a half-inch, so that it cannot even touch the bullet in a standard-length round. Then run your reference dummy round up as far as the press permits into the die (if the die is set to crimp, the die body will have to be

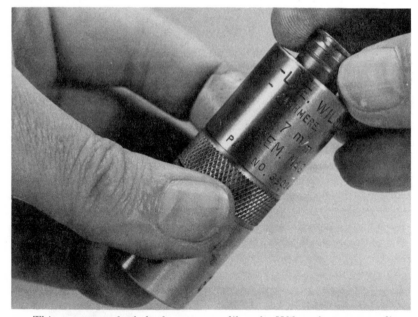

This case gauge for belted magnum calibers by Wilson features an adjustable shoulder which simplifies setting dies to make such cartridges headspace on the shoulder instead of the belt, as described in the text.

backed out a turn or so and locked in the noncrimping position). Now simply screw the seating stem back into the die until it makes *firm* contact with the bullet in your dummy cartridge. Finally, with a screwdriver, turn the seating stem *not more* than another half-turn into the die, and lock the stem in that position. Withdraw the dummy round and set it aside. Seat a bullet in a fresh case with the die so adjusted. A quick check with a caliper should reveal that the overall length of this cartridge is within a few ten-thousandths of the overall length of your reference dummy. This whole process takes about two minutes, and is reason enough to keep a collection of dummy rounds on hand for all your standard loads.

The process of using a seating die in two separate steps to seat bullets first and then to crimp case mouths on them was briefly described earlier. It merely involves using the bullet-seating stem only (with the die body backed off a turn or so) to seat bullets to the proper depth, and then backing out the seating stem and turning down the die body until the crimping shoulder comes into contact with the mouth of an empty case in the shellholder with the press ram fully raised. At this point, extremely delicate adjustments are possible, and it doesn't require much screwing-in of the die body to produce a heavy crimp.

Straight-cased cartridges are flared, as mentioned, to accept the base of the bullet without crumpling. This flaring is easily overdone, and should be nothing more than a faint outward belling of the first 1/16th inch or so of the case neck. When a bullet can barely be started with the fingers in the mouth, flaring is adequate. With many loads, however, the mouth must be belled to accept the bullet, but no crimp is desired. Cast-bullet loads in bottleneck rifle cases are an example. With such loads, the crimping shoulder inside the die cavity can be set to do no more than iron out the flare, leaving the case mouth perfectly straight rather than crimped inward onto the bullet. This is necessary, since leaving the mouth flared may interfere with chambering the round.

From this point, the crimp can be made as heavy as desired, providing there is a groove or cannelure on the bullet to receive the case mouth. If you attempt to put a roll crimp on a cartridge neck that's holding a jacketed bullet without a correctly placed cannelure, you will (a) get no crimp, and (b) ruin the entire round by swelling the shoulder. In general, if there is any justification for a crimp at all, it should be a moderate to heavy one, but it can be badly overdone. Controlling factors are the depth of the cannelure, type of bullet, and design of the die. If these factors are exceeded, the round is likely to be spoiled anyway, even if a cannelure is present. The feel of the loading press on which the work is done

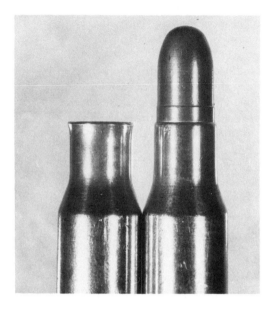

Case mouths must be flared slightly, as shown at left, to facilitate seating of cast bullets. Seating die can then be set to just remove the flare (as at right) without actually crimping.

will tell you when crimping has gone far enough. Normal crimping offers little or no extra resistance to the operation of the handle, while excessive crimping makes a quite noticeable difference in resistance at the very end of the stroke.

A good loading die is a thing of beauty and a joy for a long time, at least, if not forever, and deserves a little care. By far the most common cause of ruined dies is resizing dirty, gritty, and/or insufficiently lubricated cases in them. Amateur efforts to remove stuck cases are probably the next most frequent source of damage. Depriming stems and pins may be bent or broken by trying to decap Berdan cases or by allowing the stem's lock ring to loosen enough to permit the stem to be badly off-center. Dies are made of very high-quality steel, but none, as far as I know, are of stainless, and they will rust if neglected.

Dies are often marred by use of poorly fitting wrenches or pliers. In the typical arrangement, the locking ring around the body of the die is held in place by a set screw which presses a small soft lead pellet into the threads on the outside of the die body. These usually jam, but pliers are not needed to loosen them. A few sharp raps on the die ring with a plastic mallet, directed exactly at the set screw after it has been loosened will allow the ring to be turned freely by finger pressure only.

More and more sizing dies these days are being made with an insert of tungsten carbide which actually does the sizing. These are expensive, but worth it when large volumes of cases are to be processed, since no lubrication is required in such dies. The tungsten carbide insert, although super hard (cases come out looking burnished), may be brittle, and such dies should not be dropped or battered about with any sort of tool.

Our manufacturers of reloading dies today make a staggering array of special dies for even the wildest ideas in case forming. Almost any kind of reforming die imaginable can be special-ordered, and I know of no centerfire cartridge for which loading dies cannot be made. In general, the makers are incredibly obliging, and have already learned to solve just about any problem you're likely to run into and a few you're most unlikely to even dream of. If you have a problem, a little correspondence with the manufacturer of your dies will usually provide the answer. They also stand behind their products. The lesson in all this is to let the manufacturer use his own judgment in matters of altering or repairing loading dies. Your local machinist friend may be a hell of a machinist, but it's a safe bet he knows less about the requirements for a loading die than the people who made it.

Use your dies as they were meant to be used, and with loving care. If something feels funny in the reloading process, stop right there and run it down. Keep your cases clean and lubed, and the dies clean and protected from rust. Use only recommended tools in adjusting the dies. Consult the manufacturer about any sort of repair, projected alteration, or malfunction, as well as about any special needs in dies. Do all these things, and your dies will last as long as your rifle or pistol will, and usually longer. I have dies I've had in service for more than twenty years, and they're as good today as when they were new.

13

The Handloader's
Chronograph

Unquestionably the most important technical innovation in hand-loading during the last decade has been the development of small, portable, relatively inexpensive, and accurate chronographs. There was a day, not so long ago, when shooters had no choice but to take the word of ammunition manufacturers and publishers of reloading manuals about muzzle velocities. I do not mean to suggest that these good people deliberately misled their customers, but it was striking how the published muzzle velocities of certain brands of factory ammo were suddenly reduced at about the same time inexpensive chronographs began to come into widespread use. At about the same time, publicity on new cartridges suddenly became much more conservative. For example, one new cartridge was introduced with a claimed muzzle velocity about 800 feet per second faster than could actually be produced in the guns chambered for it and sold to the shooting public. This fact became common knowledge and the cartridge fell on its face commercially. The next new cartridge introduced by that same firm actually delivered *higher* velocities than claimed, at least in early lots, and it has been a resounding success.

A chronograph is, of course, nothing but an electronic bullet speedometer, but it has many uses other than merely satisfying a shooter's curiosity about the velocity of his reloads. Among other things, it can

Shown here is a portable chronograph that yields an elapsed-time count via illuminated nixie tubes. The lighted number is referred to a tarage table for feet per second. At right is a screen holder with a printed silver-ink circuit grid.

short-cut the load-development process and save a good deal of time, money, and components, and in addition it can help identify maximum or excessive loads.

As this is written, at least nine corporations make chronographs for the handloader, ranging in price from a low of about $50 to a high of more than $900, with several very useful models retailing very close to $100. In other words, a reloader can now have a chronograph for considerably less than the price of a good telescopic sight, or, to put it another way, he can add a chronograph to his reloading equipment without even doubling his total investment. For the serious amateur ballistician, a chronograph is almost indispensable, and they are more and more available. Two or three reloaders can chip in and buy a chronograph setup without harming the budget, and many gun clubs now have chronographs for the use of their members.

There are several varieties of electronic chronographs on the market, but by far the most common type includes an ultraprecise crystal "clock" which "ticks" at anywhere from 200,000 times per second to one million; 400,000 to 500,000 beats per second is the usual rate. Another part of the instrument is a counter which is started when the bullet arrives at a certain fixed point in space and stopped when the bullet arrives at another point. If the distance moved by the bullet between these two points is accurately known, then the number of beats counted by the chronograph during the bullet's passage can be converted to the *time* of passage and thence to feet per second. The velocity measurement thus derived is

The Sundtek is an excellent—and expensive—portable chronograph.

actually the *average* velocity of the bullet while it was between the start and stop points (remember, it was slowing down quite rapidly) and may be thought of as the bullet's speed at the midpoint between those two points. The distance from the gun's muzzle to that midpoint can be measured and the result is an *instrumental velocity* at that range. If the ballistic coefficient of the bullet is known, the velocity loss at that range can be calculated and the instrumental velocity can be corrected to *muzzle velocity.*

The electronic circuitry necessary to accomplish all this is pretty sophisticated, but the theory is just that simple. Modern integrated-circuit technology has made the hardware relatively inexpensive and incredibly accurate. The problems remaining are the most efficient and cheapest ways to notify the chronograph that the bullet has passed across the distance for which a measurement is desired, and of notifying the operator of the final result. Different manufacturers have elected to solve these problems in different ways. The most common solution to the former is the use of physical screens which are actually broken by the bullet in flight, and these have come to be called the "start screen" and the "stop screen" even with instruments which utilize other, nonmechanical means of sensing the projectile's passage. These include sonic screens which register the shock wave being created by the bullet and photoelectric ones which actually "see" the shadow of the bullet.

The "read-out" is handled in even more ways. Some instruments have a simple binomial register with a rotary switch and a "yes-no" meter. The operator rotates the switch through several positions and notes the numbers at which the meter gives a "yes" reading. He then totals these

One method of reading-out small portable chronographs is shown here. After each shot, the switch is rotated through its twelve positions. The number to which it is pointing at each setting where the yes-no meter indicates yes is written down. The total of these numbers is then referred to a tarage table for the proper feet-per-second reading. Such as system is slow, but it's inexpensive and its accuracy may be as good as that of elaborate laboratory instruments.

This portable chronograph has a digital read-out; each group of three positions on the rotary switch produces a single digit in the final count number. Less pencil-and-paper arithmetic means fewer operator errors.

numbers and refers the sum to a tarage table furnished with the chronograph, reading FPS directly from the table. With other brands, several small light bulbs will be illuminated after each shot, and the handloader adds up the numbers corresponding to the lighted bulbs and takes the total to a tarage table. Still others use the rotary switch, but with certain digital variations intended only to reduce operator errors of addition and to provide a quicker method of learning the total number of ticks of the clock which occurred while the bullet was between the screens. This is the raw number which is referred to the tarage tables.

Some of the more expensive chronographs provide a direct readout of this number, via so-called "nixie tubes" which reveal an illuminated digit. In the case of even more sophisticated, convenient, and expensive units, the readout is converted internally to feet per second by a miniaturized computer, and the operator needs not bother with arithmetic or tarage tables. What he sees is what his gun is getting, in actual FPS.

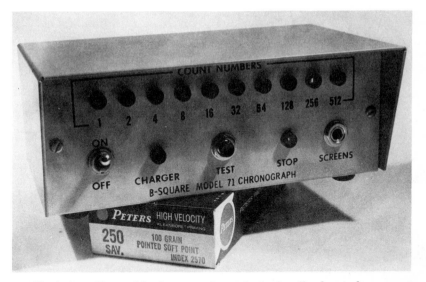

Typical small portable chronographs made for handloaders today are not much more bulky than a couple of boxes of ammunition, as well as being lightweight, battery-powered, simple to use, and extremely accurate.

The ultimate in speed, usefulness, and convenience is such a chronograph coupled with nonmechanical screens, such as those which are photoelectric. With mechanical screens, the broken screens must be replaced after each shot, which not only runs into money but forces the shooter to get up from the bench and walk out in front of the firing line for every firing. With photoelectric screens, the shooter need not ever leave his seat at the bench, and, of course, there is never a question of running out of screens nor of the expense of purchasing a fresh supply from time to time. Although the photoelectrics are expensive, they'll probably pay for themselves within a very few months or years, depending upon how much chronographing is done. The cutest I've seen (and the ones I use myself) are the Oehler Model 61 Skyscreens, which utilize light from the sky to sense the passage of the bullet. Since the bullet must only pass above these little black boxes, there is no obstruction to aiming at a distant target, and groups can be shot at the same time that each round is chronographed. They also work for shotshells, which not too many more conventional systems can handle.

Conventional, mechanical screens work in various ways. On some, the bullet *breaks* a circuit when it interrupts the physical integrity of the screen, while on others it *makes* a circuit by serving as a conductor across

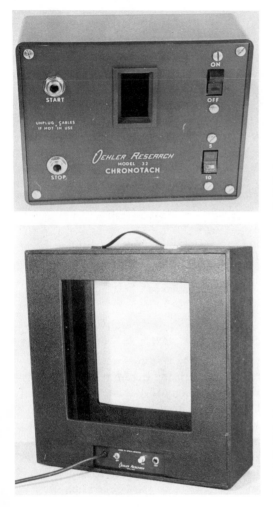

The Oehler Model 32 computes velocity and gives a readout in feet per second, one digit at a time appearing in the window. The display cycles until the next shot is fired.

A portable photoelectric screen includes a light source and an optical detector to register the passage of a bullet through the aperture. This type of screen permits group shooting with chronographed rounds, requires 110-volt power and extreme care in setting up and spacing.

which an electrical charge can short. All kinds of substances have been tried, from aluminum foil from the kitchen to pencil leads. Most screens these days are printed in conductive ink (often silver) on plastic or even plain bond paper. Depending upon the type, commercially manufactured chronograph screens cost from 10¢ to 20¢ per pair, which means per shot. A ten-round velocity-test series thus adds up to a buck or two for screens alone.

Most modern handloaders' chronographs are entirely battery powered and can be set up and used anywhere there's a safe backstop for the bullets.

The author's photoelectric chronograph screens are permanently spaced on this aluminum bar and mounted on a photographic tripod for easy transport and alignment.

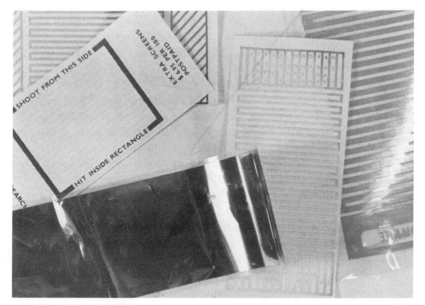

Chronograph screens may be made of paper, plastic, foil, or many other substances.

Anyone who's willing to read and follow simple instructions can operate one of these instruments, achieving a level of accuracy which is comparable in a practical sense to that of the most elaborate laboratory chronographs used by ammunition manufacturers. Some of them produce results which are comparable in that sense, and they are not necessarily among the most costly instruments.

The major bugaboo in using a portable chronograph is in the precision with which the screens themselves are spaced. A very small error in screen spacing, 1/10th inch or less, introduces a noticeable (although seldom very significant) error in readings. This is because most handloaders' chronographs are designed for relatively short spacings between screens, 5 or 10 feet being most common with a few even shorter. That 1/10th-inch error will account for an error in reading the muzzle velocity of a typical .30-06 load on the order of 7 or 8 feet per second.

With many chronograph systems, it is possible to set up the screen holders on a metal bar so that no significant change is possible from day to day. In this way, readings taken one day are at least comparable with those taken on a different day. If an error exists, it will exist in the identical amount and direction for all readings. For easy portability, a 5-foot screen spacing is about maximum for a rigid, permanent screen-holder mounting.

There are other sources of error in any chronograph system, no matter how sophisticated or expensive, and they have nothing to do with the operation of same. The crystal clock can have .05 percent error in its ticking and still remain within standard tolerances. Crystal aging, temperature, and battery voltage can contribute to this figure as well. The fact that a chronograph cannot split beats but must register a bullet's passage to the nearest whole count makes a potential error of a couple of feet per second at 3,000 FPS unavoidable. Screens are not perfect, either, and may introduce an error of screen spacing of about 1/16 inch, no matter how carefully the operator sets up. A spitzer bullet may carefully protrude more or less into the theoretical plane of the screen before it is detected and the signal sent to the chronograph. This can add one of the largest sources of error, as much as 5 or 6 feet per second at normal rifle velocities over a 5-foot screen spacing. Finally, whether the conversion from the raw count to feet per second is done with a tarage table, electronically, or by simple arithmetic, the inevitable rounding-off of a fractional foot per second may add another error of 1 FPS.

If all these sources of error were maximized in the same direction on any one shot, this "worst case" error could amount to from 3 to about 14 feet per second, depending upon velocity and screen spacing. In general, the greater the distance between screens and the lower the velocities, the smaller the "worst case" error potential becomes. As I said, these error sources are inherent in *all* chronographs from all manufacturers, although some of the latter may fail to consider some of them in the accuracy figures used in advertising. If those figures imply a "worst case" error of less than .3 percent for a velocity of 3,000 FPS with screens 10 feet apart, they may be regarded with suspicion, and will cast some doubt on other claims made for the instruments.

The distance from the muzzle of the gun to the first screen is, for handloaders' purposes, not critical, and may be adjusted so that the muzzle blast does not damage the start screen. I have used portable chronographs, however, which were affected by muzzle blast which impinged on the instrument itself. As mentioned above, temperature can affect performance and the chronograph should be kept out of direct sunlight if possible. Watch battery voltage and the tightness of cable connections, and these miraculous little black boxes are remarkably stable and free of maintenance problems. For troubleshooting, refer to the manufacturer's instructions.

The standard number of rounds in a velocity-test series is ten, and this number is recommended for precise averages. However, with very uniform loadings, it often becomes obvious by the fifth shot that additional rounds will not substantially change the average. One-, two-, or three-shot averages are very shaky evidence upon which to base reloading decisions, although they can give a very rough idea of the general range of muzzle velocities.

In view of the discussion of inherent chronograph-error sources and the well-known variations in even the most painstakingly assembled handloads, it should be apparent that a velocity series in which the extreme variation between the fastest and slowest bullet is no more than about 50 FPS is very uniform. Extreme variations of more than 100 feet per second begin to cast doubt on the load, and EVs from about 200 FPS upward are definite evidence that the load is out of balance somehow. However, if such large variations appear, take time to analyze the whole series. If, for example, nine of the ten shots reveal a normal EV and the tenth round registered either very high or very low, there's room for question of the validity of that particular shot. More testing would be required to determine whether the load is good or bad.

Within certain limits, muzzle velocity will be approximately linear with powder charge weight. As a very rough rule of thumb, within normal pressure ranges for a given powder, approximately a 10 percent change in pressure is needed to produce a 5 percent change in velocity. It may be

This handloader is checking velocities with a Herter's Mark VII chronograph. The screens in the setup shown here are almost impossible to space correctly from shot to shot, contributing a major source of error regardless of the make or model of chronograph.

deduced, then, that a handload which produces very uniform shot-to-shot velocities is also producing very uniform shot-to-shot chamber pressures. Provided the bullet being tested is known to be accurate in that individual barrel, the chances are very good that a low extreme variation in velocity tests will translate to small groups. Other factors do affect accuracy in a rifle, of course, but uniform ammunition is an excellent starting point in the search for accuracy.

This is why a chronograph can help pinpoint load formulae which are likely to be accurate, and thus save a great deal of loading and shooting time and money spent for test components. For this purpose, the actual average velocity of the load is a matter of no more than casual curiosity; the story is told by the individual velocities registered in the series of firings as related to each other.

Unacceptable extreme variations in velocities may mean any of several things, including ignition problems (wrong primer, weak firing-pin spring, etc.), an imbalance between bullet weight and powder type, and so forth, but if the velocity is near the expected maximum in that cartridge, the culprit is almost certain to be excessive pressures. As mentioned before, *high* pressures usually mean *erratic* pressures, and erratic pressures produce erratic velocity readings. If you'll check the head expansion on cases which produced the highest velocity readings when working at maximum, you'll almost invariably find it's greater than on cases which gave normal velocities. Thus the chronograph can serve as a warning of dubious pressure levels.

It can do this in another way, too. I stated above that muzzle velocity is approximately in proportion to powder charge weight *in normal pressure ranges*. However, when pressures rise *above* normal working levels, this relationship no longer obtains, and pressures can go sky-high while muzzle velocities increase very little. Thus, if your load development with a chronograph has shown that each additional grain of powder adds, say, 135 FPS to recorded velocity of a certain load when working a few grains below maximum, a sure sign that you are nearing absolute maximum is flashed by a sudden drop in the velocity increment with the addition of more powder. When another grain in the case adds only 75 extra feet per second, and still another produces only 20 or more feet per second, you have probably already exceeded a comfortable working maximum load. If these latter loads also reveal progressively greater extreme variations in velocity, the suspicion is confirmed, and can probably be proved conclusively by miking the case heads.

I have velocity series in my records which actually reveal a slight *drop* in velocity when one too many grains of powder was added to an already-maximum charge, while, at the same time, cases failed from expanded primer pockets with only one firing. Pressures in these loads were extremely dangerous, but velocities did not increase. I was getting nothing useful for my trouble, money, and the distinct hazard to which I was subjecting myself and my rifle, which is the usual case with overloads.

There comes a point at which it is not possible to drive a given bullet any faster with more of a given powder, and it is at or slightly below that point at which chamber pressures begin to go out of sight.

One of the greatest values in a portable chronograph is the precise identification of that point.

14

Loading for Accuracy

The word "uniformity" has appeared throughout this text because it contains the real secret to handloading satisfaction. The greatest advantage a reloader has over the ammunition factories is that he does not have to make a profit on his time, and can go to any lengths he wishes to preserve cartridge-to-cartridge uniformity. True, he can hand-tailor loads to the demonstrated preferences of his individual firearms, but even that is to no avail unless he can assemble the ammo to considerably closer tolerances than a manufacturer can who must produce tens of thousands of rounds per hour at a competitive price.

When we speak of accuracy, we are speaking of uniformity; it is the great key to accurate handloads. Only when techniques for uniformity are so standardized that they can be taken for granted can we begin to search through more esoteric realms for new breakthroughs in accuracy.

First, we must answer the question "How accurate *is* 'accurate'?" Obviously, the answer varies widely. A woodchuck shooter who does most of his shooting on the far side of 300 yards would laugh out loud at the African professional hunter's concept of accuracy. The former demands at least minute-of-angle accuracy, while the latter is only interested in minute-of-rhinoceros accuracy in his big .470 double rifle. A far-gone benchrest competitor might sneer at both of them. Joe Deerhunter worries

more about the carryability and handleability of his rifle than its grouping ability, and may cheerfully settle for 3-inch groups at 100 yards, knowing that such a weapon will reliably put every deer he'll ever shoot at on
the ground if he does his part. Obviously, there is no absolute standard of
accuracy against which any and all rifles and pistols can be judged. It's up
to each individual handloader to decide, in planning his load, what degree of accuracy is necessary to the load's purpose. If he finds he can
exceed his minimum requirements, so much the better; if not, he at least
knows whether the load has succeeded or failed.

Accuracy in rifled arms is usually described in terms of minutes of
angle. If you imagine yourself standing at the center of a perfect circle,
that circle could be divided into 21,600 minutes of angle. A minute of
angle, being a measurement of arc, is a minute of angle at any range. At
100 yards, it figures out to 1.047168 inches. For practical purposes, this is
so close to an even 1 inch that handloaders consider a rifle which groups
inside 1 inch at 100 yards a minute-of-angle rifle. However, to be a *true*
minute-of-angle rifle, it should also group in 2 inches at 200 yards, 3
inches at 300 yards, and so on, out to its maximum practical range. One
minute of angle at 1,000 yards, for example, is 10 inches, and there are
rifles and there are riflemen capable of minute-of-angle performance even
at that range.

You will *hear* of a great many more standard, off-the-shelf sporting
rifles which are capable of minute-of-angle accuracy than you will ever
see. If you worry a lot about the apparent fact that everybody else's deer
rifle is good for a "minute" (according to the owner) while yours seems to
average no better than, say, 1.75 minutes of angle (MOA), your distress
will be considerably relieved by actually shooting those other red-hot
sporters. A couple of 1-MOA groups do not an MOA rifle make; the long-
run average is what counts.

The accuracy potential of a rifle is inherent in many different parts
of the gun and ammunition. The quality of the barrel itself is probably
the most important single item, along with the bedding of wood to steel
throughout the arm, the trigger, the lock time, and several other factors.
An entire book could easily be written on the subject of "tuning" a rifle
for optimum accuracy, and I have no room here for such a discussion.
However, proper load development is an essential part of such tuning,
and that *is* relevant to our topic.

One thing must be understood about the barrel, and it is that even
the stiffest, most massive rifle barrel vibrates like a tuning fork when fired.
A lighter barrel's vibrations have a greater amplitude than those of a bull
barrel, but they all vibrate. The vibration causes the muzzle to move, but

the direction of the movement is unpredictable. In the case of a perfectly bedded barreled action, the movement should be perfectly vertical, assuming a perfect barrel. Most barrels have some lateral component to their vibrations, with the muzzle swinging in a circle or an oval at some angle.

Now follow this carefully, for it will explain some seemingly mysterious things you will experience in your load testing. The barrel begins to vibrate as soon as the powder charge begins to burn, and the vibration continues throughout the time the bullet takes to move down the barrel and depart the muzzle. This period is called the "barrel time" of the bullet, and it varies from load to load, depending upon the burning characteristics of the powder and the quantity being burned. Let's assume we have one of those perfect barrels, perfectly bedded, which vibrates only in the vertical plane. Furthermore, let's assume that the first shot fired delivers the bullet at the muzzle when the muzzle happens to be at its maximum upward displacement on its vibration cycle. If the next shot fired happens to have a very slightly different barrel time, the bullet may arrive at the muzzle when it's at its maximum downward displacement. Although the physical displacement of the axis of the bore at the muzzle may be very small, it is nonetheless a real factor in grouping; those two bullets were actually launched in slightly different directions and the first will arrive at a measurably higher impact point on target than will the second one.

From this, the importance of consistent barrel time from shot to shot can be realized, and near-perfect uniformity in all factors in the load is the key to consistent barrel time. If the barrel in question happens to vibrate in, say, an oval pattern (which most of them do), the displacement of successive shots due to varying barrel times will be lateral as well as vertical.

This vibration phenomenon, by the way, explains why a lower-velocity load with a heavier bullet will occasionally register a higher point of impact at 100 yards than a speedy, light-bullet load, contrary to apparent logic and the laws of physics. It also explains why a given powder and charge will sometimes shoot to a different point of impact than another load which drives the same bullet at an identical velocity, a point of some importance to handloaders striving to adjust the point of impact of a low-velocity small-game load relative to that of a full-power loading in the same rifle.

Accuracy in rifles, of course, involves a host of factors other than consistent barrel time. Probably the most important single element in accuracy after a high-quality, well-bedded barrel is the bullet. Some of the characteristics of "good" bullets have already been discussed, as has proper bullet seating relative to the rifling. The basic key to accuracy could be said to be good bullets in a good barrel. It's true that one rifle may shoot smaller groups with one bullet while another, identical arm does its best work with a different bullet, but these differences are usually quite small. A good bullet is a good bullet in *any* rifle, and a rifle which shoots small groups with one good bullet almost always does nearly as well with any other equally good bullet. Bullet selection is critical to accuracy, but reading and talking with handloaders experienced with your cartridge shortens the search for the right projectile for your purposes.

As we have said, the right powder and charge weight is also important to finest accuracy, and here individual rifles may show rather wide differences. It's well worth experimenting with as many powders as may be appropriate in the cartridge in question, because now and then one of them will turn out to be exactly what a particular rifle prefers, delivering dramatically better groups than any other propellant. This will not regularly be the case, but it happens often enough to be worth trying when the very finest possible accuracy is the goal in a given rifle.

Most of the rest of the factors recognized as vital to best accuracy lie in the cartridge case and the techniques for preparing and loading it. The portion of the case's anatomy most critical to accuracy is the neck, the part which holds the bullet. Ideally, all case necks in a lot should be exactly the same length, exactly the same thickness all around their circumference, and should grip their bullets with exactly the same tension, not too much and not too little. Uniformity in case-neck length is easily achieved by careful trimming, deburring, and chamfering. Case-neck thickness is another matter. The right thickness must be related to the rifle chamber in which the cases are to be fired and to the internal dimensions of the die in which they will be resized. If necks are thinned too much, the die may not reduce the internal diameter enough to provide proper grip on the bullets. Necks can be thinned and evened up by inside reaming or outside turning with the neck supported on a close-fitting mandrel. Inside reaming can be performed with special attachments offered for use with several of the case-trimming tools on the market, with special reamers furnished by die manufacturers, or with a boring-bar tool made by Lee. Any of these tools will do a good job, but the benchrest shooters who tend to go to the ultimate extremes in search of accuracy almost universally prefer the outside turning technique. This can be done on a lathe, of course, but several small, ultraprecise. hand tools are available (from Marquart Precision, Dewey, Hart, and others) which are capable of holding neck thickness all the way around a case to plus or

One of several satisfactory methods of inside reaming of case necks: a special die with a reamer which is turned with a tap wrench.

minus .0001″. Neck turning is tedious work at best, and is not worth the trouble, according to my experiments, on hunting rifles. Very accurate field varmint rifles, say those averaging under ¾-inch groups at 100 yards with unaltered case necks, will show a small but definite improvement in accuracy with processed necks, and serious bench rifles absolutely demand turning necks. Some winning benchresters do nothing special to their brass except to use cases from the same lot and to trim and turn case necks, but they regard these things as essential.

The other end of the case comes in for attention from other serious accuracy buffs. The flash hole, through which the primer flash reaches the powder charge, should be uniform from case to case in terms of both diameter and length. The idea is that this contributes to uniformity of ignition. Flash holes can be gauged so that cases can be sorted into lots with holes of uniform diameter, or a twist drill of the correct diameter can be used to enlarge all flash holes in a lot of cases to the same diameter. However, flash holes which have been materially enlarged will cause high pres-

This hand-turned case-neck turner shaves necks to uniform thickness within .0001 inch, and is a must for ultimate accuracy. This tool is by Marquart.

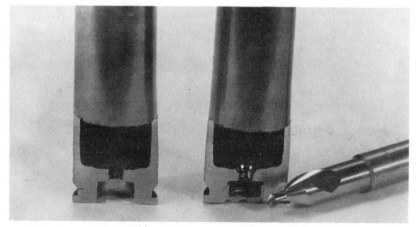

The Brown Flash Hole Uniformer removes internal burrs and produces flash holes of uniform length as well as diameter, improving accuracy somewhat.

sures, and should be avoided. On small rifle cases (the only kind, usually, which deserve such meticulous treatment) flash holes are best kept not smaller than .081″ or larger than .089″. A #45 twist drill will produce a uniform .082″ hole, which seems about right. The latest rage among benchresters, as this is written, are tools which chamfer the inside end of the flash hole for uniform length as well as diameter.

The seating of the bullet is of considerable importance to accuracy, not only as to the matter of seating depth, but also seating straightness. Special seating dies for use in bench-mounted tools are popular which have provisions for holding the case and the bullet in perfect alignment throughout the process of seating. This is supposed to result in better concentricity and a loaded round in which the axis of the bullet is parallel to and identical with that of the case. There's no doubt at all that this does indeed reduce group sizes, but, again, it's mostly the superaccurate rifles which can benefit. Varmint shooters may find such special seating dies a good investment, but no big-game hunter ever will.

Two bullet-seating dies for the .22-250. That at left features precise straight-line seating of the bullet by means of the sliding tube that holds bullet and case in alignment throughout the seating step. It's more expensive—but better accuracy may result.

There are tools for everything in handloading, and there are tools made which measure the crookedness of loaded ammunition. The Brown Precision "Little Wiggler" is especially useful for this purpose, because it not only indicates the amount of "run-out" or crookedness of a seated bullet, but incorporates a little jack by means of which the round can actually be straightened by the few thousandths of an inch usually required. This tool will also measure the thickness of case necks to within .0005"; even benchresters concede that .002" is adequate case-neck uniformity. If loaded rounds are crooked enough, no gauge is needed to spot the problem; simply roll the round across a smooth surface and watch the point of the bullet. If it is seen to rotate in a small circle as the cartridge rolls, it is tilted enough to affect accuracy. The rule of thumb is that each .001" of crookedness in the bullet as seated will result in a displacement on target at 100 yards of about ⅛ inch. Most factory ammunition reveals a misalignment of from .002" to .006", and military ammo is about the same. Each shooter can decide for himself how important to his purposes this element of accuracy is, but a fair rule might be as follows: for benchrest shooting, maximum acceptable bullet tilt of .0005"; for serious long-range varminting, not more than .001" run-out; for general hunting, including big game, not more than .004", preferably less.

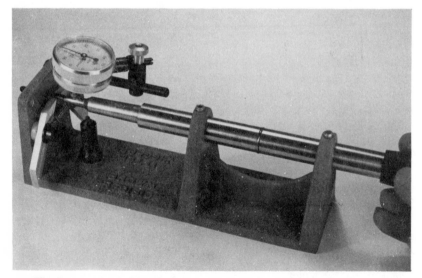

The Brown "Little Wiggler" can measure either lack of bullet concentricity or neck thickness uniformity.

It should go without saying, of course, that all these cunning efforts to build the utmost accuracy into handloaded ammunition will be for naught if the cases used are not carefully sorted, and preferably all of the same lot. It might be worth repeating here, too, that uniformity of powder charge weight is crucial to accuracy. Charges should be within .2 grain of the same weight for any sort of shooting where accuracy is a factor, and within plus or minus .1 grain where it is paramount. Handweighing each charge is the way to be certain, but a skilled operator with a familiar powder measure of high quality can learn to throw charges this uniform, at least with certain powders. Few or no benchrest shooters that I know handweigh charges, even for match shooting, but they're real experts with their powder measures.

One more thing: Handloads for the ultimate in accuracy are never crimped, except in a few handgun cartridges.

And what has all this to do with reloading for ordinary hunting and plinking? Well, every rifleman is interested in accuracy as a general concept, and most of us get the bug, sooner or later, to see just how well our sporters can be made to shoot. The real accuracy buffs have improved the breed, so to speak, in the same way that improvements pioneered in the superspecialized Indianapolis racing cars have filtered down to the family station wagon. If this chapter has done nothing else, perhaps it has included information from which the hunter and plinker can judge whether his guns are doing their best, however good or badly that may be, and in which direction to look for improvement when the accuracy virus bites. It's a virus to which *no* handloader ever becomes immune.

15

Loading for the Hunting Field

During the last twenty years, I've not fired more than a handful of factory cartridges in rifles or pistols at live game—and I've been blessed with an exceptionally full and far-ranging hunting career, including two African safaris. I'm amused to hear hunters express amazement that I'll risk the time and expense of an elaborate hunting trip on my "home-made" ammunition, and express concern for my physical safety when I expect to deal with dangerous game.

The attitude of these well-meaning people seems to be that hand-loads may be OK for plinking and target practice, or even for an occasional deer hunt, but that there must be something inferior about them when the chips are down and the stakes are high. The truth is that, if rim-fire ammo is counted, I've experienced far more trouble with factory-loaded cartridges than with my own reloads. In fact, I have yet to have a misfire with a handloaded round while hunting. A few months ago, I went up against a wounded and very angry African lion at just 30 yards with a magazine full of handloaded cartridges in a wildcat rifle, and the lion failed to survive the encounter. I've also shot seven Cape buffalo bulls (and stood as back-up gun on three more) and one record-size leopard, all with handloads—and without the slightest qualm.

The author killed this record leopard with a .45-70, the same cartridge with which Custer's men were armed—but reloading boosted the ballistics far beyond anything Sitting Bull ever dreamed of and produced an instantaneous kill.

One of the reasons for this confidence in handloads is that I am aware of one paramount fact as I assemble cartridges for the hunting field, and it is that nothing less than absolute mechanical reliability is acceptable in such rounds. *Perfect* functioning, feeding from the magazine, chambering, firing, extraction, and ejection are the *first* considerations in hunting handloads. These things must not be compromised for any other performance factor. If they are, the trophy of a lifetime on the hunt of a lifetime may be lost, not to mention the fact that such compromises can get a hunter killed.

Mechanical reliability is not at all difficult to ensure. For hunting loads, I prefer to use brass which has been fired once in the hunting rifle, but which has not been fired more than two or three times at most. Ideally, brass which has been fired, resized, and reloaded for the hunt de-

livers the smallest odds on a malfunction. That first firing is likely to reveal any inherent flaw in the case (extremely rare, but possible) and to
expand the case to fit that particular chamber.

For hunting, I always full-length resize my cases; this avoids the occasional swelled case which may not only fail to chamber but may jam the
rifle hopelessly under a hunter's frantic efforts to force it home. Naturally,
I make certain that cases for hunting are duly sorted and carefully
trimmed, chamfered, and deburred. If my dies are adjusted correctly,
these few precautions take care of about 99 percent of all potential mechanical malfunctions. The other 1 percent can be positively eliminated
by making certain that the loads I'm using are not too hot, and by careful
attention to correct seating depths of the bullets (really a part of die
adjustment).

A powder charge which develops excessive pressure, remember, can
cause difficult extraction or even stick a case solidly in the chamber,
making it impossible to open the rifle's action. That can be avoided, of
course, by keeping hunting loads distinctly below maximum levels. But
there's another factor which has not been discussed before, and it is
ambient temperature, or, more precisely, powder temperature at the
moment of firing. This temperature can make quite a bit of difference in
chamber pressures, so much so that artillerymen must compensate for
temperature in calculating the range at which howitzer shells will land
with a given muzzle elevation. The hunting rifleman has no such intricate
problems, but extreme temperature variations must be kept in mind
when developing handloads. If, for example, he's working up a load at his
home in Michigan on a chilly spring day, and intends to use that load on
a javelina hunt in the Arizona desert where temperatures may be 50° to
60° higher, he'll do well to keep that differential in mind as he
approaches maximum charge levels. It's very unlikely that intelligently
developed loads will be pushed into dangerous pressure regions, even by a
temperature variation of 100°, but the point of impact may vary significantly. Conversely, a hunter who develops loads during a Texas summer
should keep in mind that his zero may shift quite a bit when those cartridges are fired at a mule deer in the Colorado Rockies on a frosty
November morning.

This is an extremely complex subject, and any general rule is likely
to exhibit all sorts of exceptions. Some types of powder are much more
sensitive to temperature variations than others, and the type of cartridge
and density of loading can affect results. Temperature vs. velocity tables
have been published in the *Speer Reloading Manual,* in Ackley's *Hand-*

book for Shooters and Reloaders, by duPont, and in Handloader magazine. They do not necessarily agree in detail, and, as mentioned, warn of many exceptions.

Here are some very rough rules which may help a little. Only extreme variations are significant, say powder temperature changes of more than 30° from a "normal" 70° F. From 70° down to about zero, a typical load may lose about 100 FPS, or gain about the same amount of velocity from 70° up to 100°. Certain powders must be watched more closely than others, and these include all the Ball types, most double-based propellants, and the old, surplus H-4831 and IMR 4350. Heavy charges and high loading densities tend to increase pressure changes with changing temperature.

In general, temperature variations are unlikely to change 100-yard points of impact more than a couple of inches, at most, between 0° and 100°, but at very long ranges could conceivably cause a miss on deer-size targets. They are also unlikely to bring about dangerous pressure rises, but this shouldn't be taken for granted where loads are already maximum. Best bet is to cut back a grain or two of powder for hunting in very hot climates. We used to believe that a change in primers, from standard types to magnums, was indicated even with nonmagnum-type propellants in extremely cold weather. Recent tests have cast doubt on this theory, but they haven't given any indication that such a primer switch is undesirable either.

The point to remember is that the actual temperature of the powder at the moment of firing is what's important, not the air temperature. Ammunition carried inside a hunter's outer clothing in subzero weather will be much warmer than the air, and ammo left in the direct rays of the sun, even in mild weather, can reach temperatures of 150°, which can be dangerous. Even cartridges stored in the closed trunk of a car in direct sunlight may get much too hot for safety. All these things are as true of factory ammunition as of handloads, of course.

Bullet seating has an effect on mechanical reliability which must be determined in each individual rifle, just as temperature variations in zero should be checked out in your rifle. A fairly common lament among reloaders is that they did all load-development firing on the rifle range by single-loading the cartridges and failed to test the load's feeding qualities until it was too late. Sometimes a roundnosed bullet will be balky in a magazine in which spitzers of the same weight and seating depth behave beautifully, or vice versa. Occasionally, seating a bullet just a tenth of an inch deeper or shallower will smooth out the all-important quick trip from magazine to chamber. The only way to make certain is to load five or so dummy rounds which are identical to the planned loading except that they have no primers or powder, and run them through the rifle. Try working the action at different speeds; now and then a load will feed perfectly when the action is slammed open and closed but hang up when it is worked deliberately. Or it may be the other way around. In any case, try everything you can think of to make trouble in feeding—holding the rifle muzzle up and muzzle down, even on its side. If your round feeds flawlessly in such tests, it's a safe bet for the hunting field.

Finally, work every single cartridge through the magazine and into and out of the chamber when you have finished loading the lot for your hunting trip. Make no exceptions; take not even one round which hasn't successfully made the trip through the rifle at least once. This should be done with due consideration of the fact that live ammo is being handled and that the rifle will be fully loaded for a few seconds with each round. It should be done in a safe place with the muzzle pointed in a safe direction at all times, and with the fingers nowhere near the trigger. If the gun has a three-position safety, so much the better. In the middle position, usually, the bolt can be operated but the arm will not fire. Even so, the whole operation is best carried out on a rifle range with the muzzle pointed at the backstop. When it has been successfully completed, you can be certain that there will be no malfunctions in the field, no bullets seated too long, no cases sized not quite enough, and no other oddball foul-ups to cost you a shot at game. I was following my own advice with a lot of .350 Remington Magnum cartridges I'd loaded for a jaguar hunt in Mexico when I discovered that the bolt would not close behind two of the rounds. Examination revealed that a self-operating "universal" shell-holder I'd been using in my loading press had deformed the rims of these two cases so that, although they chambered properly, the bolt could not close. Needless to say, those cartridges never saw the interior of Mexico. A jaguar can be a formidable beast, especially when wounded in his jungle strongholds at night, and the thought of one of those freakish rounds on top of the magazine stack still gives me the shudders. I have not seen that particular cartridge deformity before or since in my reloading and certainly would never have been looking for it in a visual inspection of the loaded rounds. But my inviolable rule of checking *every* round of hunting ammo through the rifle alerted me to a totally unforeseen problem.

The importance of selecting the right bullet for the hunting job at hand has been mentioned before, but it may appropriately be re-emphasized here. Although accuracy, flatness of trajectory, retained energy, and similar good things are certainly important, a hunting bullet is no good if its expansion and penetration capabilities are not matched

These three bullets, recovered from big game, show perfect performance—excellent expansion and retention of most of the original weight for maximum penetration. Cores and jackets are still together.

to the game and the hunting conditions. Fortunately, it's not necessary to make a choice between all these qualities; most good hunting bullets *are* accurate and have good ballistic coefficients. Where some lingering doubt may exist, however, you will never err by choosing the bullet of known impact performance, even if you must give up an unimportant half-inch or inch in grouping or 100 foot-pounds of muzzle energy.

Deer hunters in particular concern themselves about what is called "brush-bucking" ability in their bullets, as though they expected a certain slug to cut a cord of firewood and stack it enroute to a whitetail in the thickets. The truth is that there is really no such thing as a real brush-buster of a rifle bullet. In shooting at a Botswana Cape buffalo in 1974, I had a .41 caliber, 400-grain bullet at 2,400 FPS deflect from a small sapling. This slug had all of the usual qualifications listed for a brush-

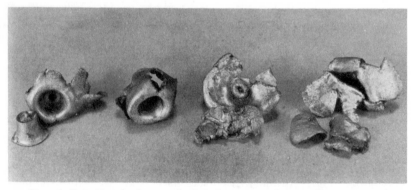

Four bullets that broke up, shed their cores, and generally came to pieces on big-game animals.

bucker—fat, heavy, roundnosed, and traveling at a modest velocity—yet it deflected about 6 feet in traveling only 12 yards from where it struck the mopane tree. Fortunately, the buff was already heart-shot and dying, but neither he nor I knew it at that moment. That it hit him at all was pure luck, and would have been very bad luck if he'd been unwounded.

The selection of very heavy bullets in hopes of improving penetration in brush may be self-defeating, since such slugs in a rifling twist to which they are barely suited may be inadequately stabilized. A marginally stable bullet tends to be deflected by a greater amount and from a smaller encounter with a twig than a normal-weight bullet humming along, sound asleep. In the last analysis, it's far better to pick a hole in the brush than to count any bullet's bulling its way through a heavy screen of brush to a half-seen target. If you doubt it, try a few rounds of your favorite brush-buster through heavy brush on a cardboard box or some similarly large target. You'll be disappointed, but at least you'll be relieved of the need to worry about the obstacle penetration of projectiles for your hunting handloads and can concentrate on more important decisions.

Even the most ferocious of big-bore bullets are subject to deflection. This sapling turned a 400-grain, .41-caliber, roundnosed bullet at moderate velocity. The bullet deflected almost 6 feet in the next 12 yards of travel.

Loading for semiautomatic rifles for hunting is one of these, since such arms have several special problems. Most of those on the market today are gas-operated, but some older models use the long-recoil system. In either case, the pressures developed by handloads must be regulated rather delicately for satisfactory functioning. If pressures rise too high, some parts of the rifle may be battered in the slam-bang of autoloading operation. If they fail to reach proper levels, the rifle may not cycle at all, in effect becoming a rather elaborate single-shot, or it may fire and jam with each shot. Also, the semiautos do not have the powerful initial extraction effort of a bolt-action, and high pressures may stick cases in an auto more quickly than in manually operated types. Maximum powder charge weights in self-loaders usually turn out to be about 2 to 4 grains below those which work well in a bolt gun, but your particular rifle can provide the answers with careful experimenting. Full-length resizing is usually mandatory in a semiauto, and a special small-base sizing die may be required. To some extent, these same remarks may apply with equal strength to slide-action weapons and, in lesser degree, to certain lever-actions.

In many ways, loading for the hunting field produces ammunition more like that made in commercial ammo factories than does any other phase of handloading. If Remington, Federal, and Winchester could tailor ammo specifically to your rifle, however, you would still have one major reason for reloading your hunting cartridges, and that would be the opportunity to select precisely the right bullet for your game species, under the conditions and in the terrain in which you hunt it, and according to your personal technique and style of hunting.

And that reason alone is well worth the trouble, entirely aside from the satisfaction all hunter-reloaders derive from using ammunition they figured out and built with their own hands.

16

Special-Purpose Loads for Rifles and Pistols

A "special-purpose" handload may be defined as one of such limited applications that little or no loading data is to be found for it in standard reference material. There are many such loadings, and they provide some of the real fun to be had in handloading.

A fairly common example is the turkey load for a big-game rifle. In many areas, turkey seasons coincide with deer seasons and the rifle is a legal weapon for gobblers, but an expanding bullet at full velocity through the middle of a turkey makes such a mess of a magnificent game bird, not to mention a Christmas dinner, that no sportsman tries it a second time. Such a bullet in the head or neck, or carefully placed to break the back, will do a clean job on the bird, but such shots are difficult, to put it mildly, beyond about 50 yards even for experts. The answer is a separate handload, especially formulated for the purpose, which has a point of impact relative to the big-game load in the same rifle such that it can be used without changing the sights and, hopefully, without all sorts of mental gymnastics. Finally, it must not be destructive even with a center shot, so that the hunter can simply aim where the bird is biggest at any reasonable range.

For most cartridges, such loads are no great trick to work out. The overriding consideration is muzzle velocity, which should not materially

The payoff for the time and trouble spent developing a special turkey load for a centerfire big-game rifle: a gobbler potted at long range and without meat destruction.

exceed about 2,000 FPS regardless of caliber or bullet type. Even full-jacketed military bullets can do unacceptable damage at high velocity, as anyone knows who has tried standard military ammunition on turkeys from his .308 or .30-06. Velocity alone is destructive; indeed, if forced to the choice, I'd prefer a soft-nosed slug at 2,000 FPS to a high-speed "solid."

As usual, the first decision is the bullet. Nonexpanding bullets are available in almost any caliber from at least one of several sources. They are—or were—manufactured for target-shooting purposes by Norma in many popular calibers, and by a few custom bullet makers in a more limited selection of diameters. Cast bullets made of some such hard lead alloy as Linotype metal serve very nicely, and molds are available in most sizes. Military bullets can occasionally be purchased either loose or in obsolete ammo which can be broken down for components, and the range of calibers is greater than you may suppose, including 6.5 and 7mm, .303,

Four different approaches to a turkey-load bullet for centerfire rifle cartridges. From left, a full-jacketed military bullet in the .222 Remington, a full-jacketed sporting bullet (Speer) in the 6mm Remington, an FMJ .30 M-1 Carbine bullet in the .308 WCF, and a hard-cast lead alloy pistol bullet in the .35 Remington.

8mm, .30 caliber in several weights, and others. Remington-Peters sells full-jacketed bullets in .224. If there is a choice, the lighter bullets in a given caliber usually work better because they can be stabilized in normal rifling twists at the modest velocities we have in mind for turkey loads.

Powder loads should *always* be selected from among the faster-burning numbers. The very slow-burning propellants occasionally produce something called a "pressure excursion" when used in reduced loads. Pressure excursion is a somewhat mysterious phenomenon which has yet to be satisfactorily explained and which, so far, has defied all efforts to reproduce it at will under laboratory conditions. That it occurs, however, cannot be doubted. Fortunately, it is easily avoided by the handloader, by adopting as a rule the practice of using slow-burning powders (say, relative quicknesses of about that of IMR 4350 and slower) only in near-full-power charges. Never reduce a loading with one of these powders by more than 10 percent below listed maximums.

With a powder, or several candidate powders, selected, the charge weight which will deliver about 2,000 FPS must be determined, usually by extrapolation since loading data for most high-velocity cartridges do not extend downward to this range. At this point, one of the reloading manuals which has data arranged for each combination of cartridge, bullet, and powder in a horizontal line of ascending velocity levels comes in handy. Hornady's and Sierra's manuals are examples. A little close study of the data for your turkey cartridge with the bullet weight closest to the one you plan to use will reveal that there is a more or less linear relationship between powder charge weight and velocity. For example, you may find that approximately 1.5 grains of powder are required to produce each additional 100 FPS. Although the lowest listed charge may give a velocity considerably higher than 2,000 FPS, this relationship should hold pretty well down to that speed. Thus, if the lightest listed charge gives 3,000 FPS at 47 grains, you can try 10 times 1.5 grains, or 15 grains less than 47, or 32 grains of that powder for an expected 2,000 FPS. Such downward extrapolation is quite safe, although *upward* extrapolation of charges is never recommended.

Another possible source of data on low-velocity loads is the fairly voluminous literature now published for cast bullet shooting, especially including the *Lyman Cast Bullet Handbook*. However, much of this literature deals with the fastest-burning powders, and some caution must be exercised in substituting jacketed slugs for cast bullets at maximum levels. The jacketed bullets will produce more pressure, and, usually, lower velocities. Also, a seemingly small charge of a fast-burning powder can produce high pressure, even in a big case if warnings about maximum charges are ignored.

There is, of course, no way to adjust velocities to a precise level without access to a chronograph, but these turkey-load velocities need not be on the money. If the point of impact in your rifle is usable, it really doesn't matter whether the velocity is 1,850 or 2,100 FPS. Properly placed, either will make short work of a turkey and leave an edible carcass.

Sometimes the first load tried will work out well in terms of relative point of impact. If I can get a turkey load to strike within an inch or so below or above my regular big-game loading for the same rifle at 100 yards, I'm satisfied. With such a load, any gobbler I get a fair crack at up to about 150 yards is meat for the freezer. More often, the turkey load will display a maddening tendency to strike several inches low and perhaps to one side or the other. This signals some patient experimenting, with different charges of the same powder and/or with other propellants. Remember the discussion of barrel vibrations and barrel time; the experiments are simply an effort to find a load which enjoys a serendipitous relationship with that particular barrel. It may come anywhere, unpredictably, but you can almost invariably find it if you keep looking. Of all the rifles for which I've loaded over the years, only one absolutely defies my every attempt to work out a turkey load which can be used without making a sight adjustment. And, although I've tried more than a hundred different combinations in this rifle, I still haven't given up.

What we've termed a "turkey load" here has many other uses. It will work equally well on small and medium-size game like fox (without destroying the pelt) up to about javelina. It's usually a good pest load for porcupines, armadillos, and the occasional quail-eating feral domestic cat. And, being cheap, it's a first-class informal target and year-round plinking load, without much recoil and blast. Many of my rifles remain zeroed for the "turkey" load at 100 yards at all times except during big-game seasons.

Another useful special-purpose load is the "squib," which is nothing more than a centerfire rifle load designed to approach absolute noiselessness. It's entirely possible to develop a squib in most big-game cartridges which are so quiet that the sound of the bullet striking the target is actually louder than the muzzle "blast." Such loads are, necessarily, for very short range, usually no more than about 25 yards but they can be surprisingly accurate at such ranges. They usually require a sight change, but now and again I've had one take the same sight-setting at 25 yards that my full-power loads required for a 200-yard zero.

The obvious use for a squib is gallery shooting (with an appropriate bullet trap) in the basement or garage, where target practice can be carried out without attracting the ire of the neighbors or the attention of the police. Squibs are also suitable for shooting the smallest pests, such as sparrows or rats.

Velocity is hardly important in a squib, since the noise level is the controlling factor, but most squibs will chronograph somewhere between 500 and 900 FPS, and energy delivery will probably approximate that of a .22 rimfire cartridge—which means that these silent little loads mustn't be treated with contempt. Every safety precaution required for any kind of firearm is indicated.

The bullet is the chief problem in a squib-loading project. Jacketed slugs are out; at these velocities, they may stick in the barrel! The lightest possible cast bullet for the caliber should be chosen for any kind of stability at such reduced velocities in normal rifling twists. The powder charge is easy; in just about any cartridge of .30-06 volume or less, a good squib load will be found somewhere between 1.5 and about 4 grains of Hercules

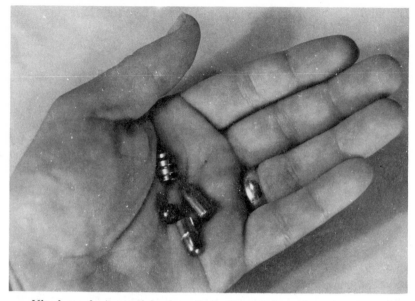

Ultralow-velocity squib loads can be built around a variety of projectiles, including buckshot of the proper size, cast wadcutters, full-jacketed, lightweight military bullets, or commercial "plinkers." Light weight is the key to stability in normal rifling twists at abnormally low speeds.

Squib loads often develop too little pressure to expand the brass case for good obturation, resulting in an accumulation of soot on the case and in the chamber. Chambers should be cleaned thoroughly before firing high-pressure loads after you've been doing much squib shooting.

Bullseye powder. Start at the lower charge weight and vary the load by
.2-grain increments until a satisfactory compromise between noise and
short-range accuracy is located. Bullseye being one of the fastest-burning
of all powders, care must be taken to avoid double-charging.

Brass which is used for squib loads should be segregated or marked,
or both, so that it cannot be used again for full-power loadings. The
reason is that the force of the firing-pin blow in some rifles can drive the
case into the chamber so that the shoulder is set back slightly. The pressure of the squib is insufficient to fire-form the case again, and a rimless
case may wind up with excess headspace. This is no problem with squib
loads, but could be dangerous at high pressures. Squib cases need not be
resized at all, usually, but they tend to get very sooty since they don't ob-
turate the breech very solidly. The chamber will get just as sooty, and
needs special cleaning after a session of squib firing.

Turkey loads and squib loads are just two examples of types of ammunition which you cannot purchase from Remington or Winchester,

A full spectrum of loads for the .308 Winchester cartridge are lined up here.
From left, a quiet, low-velocity squib (cast bullet), a turkey-and-small-game load
(110-grain military FMJ bullet), a deer load (150-grain softpoint at full velocity),
a varmint load (130-grain hollowpoint), a big-game load (165-grain softpoint),
and a brush-buster-and-bear load (200-grain Nosler).

and which extend the versatility of your rifle to previously undreamt-of limits. Only your needs and your imagination restrict the variety of such low-velocity loads. Would you like to use your deer rifle on squirrels during the off-season, just to keep your eye in? No reason not to; just use your squib bullet (which might even be a buckshot run through the correct bullet-sizing die) and adjust the velocity wherever in the range of 1,200 to 1,400 FPS you find minute-of-squirrel's-head accuracy at about 50 feet.

These three loads form the low end of what might be termed a full spectrum of loads for a single rifle. The other pieces of the spectrum would include a varmint load using lightly jacketed, lightweight bullets at maximum velocity. This one is for jackrabbits and woodchucks at ranges of at least 200 yards, depending on your rifle's inherent accuracy and sighting equipment. There would also be the standard deer load, of course, which is probably the first one you developed and which is the only one ever worked up by all too many handloaders who haven't realized that you don't have to make a big bang to have shooting fun. Another load in the spectrum might be a heavy-game load, if the cartridge is suitable, utilizing a heavy, strongly constructed bullet at medium velocities.

Obviously, some cartridges lend themselves to full-spectrum loading better than others. Those which do are the medium-capacity cases between the calibers of .264 and 8mm, roughly. You will never make a brown-bear cartridge out of a .243 or .250 Savage, nor will your .338 or .350 Remington Magnum prove to be an adequate varminter, but the vast majority of rifles in use in the U.S. today as big-game weapons can be far more flexible, more fun, and more use throughout the year than factory ammo alone can make them.

Some of the belted magnums, especially the 7mm, work reasonably well as full-spectrum rifles, although their cavernous cases make development of squibs and turkey loads somewhat trying at times. But all of them lend themselves to what may be called "stairstep" loading. By this is meant loading them down to duplicate the performance of smaller cartridges of identical caliber. The 7mm Remington Magnum can be made into a perfectly good 7 × 57mm Mauser, .284 WCF, or .280 Remington. The .300 Winchester or Weatherby Magnums convert nicely to .30-06s, .308s, .300 Savages, or even .30-30s. The .350 Norma Magnum can handily duplicate the .350 Remington Magnum, the .35 Whelen, the .358 WCF, or the .35 Remington. There's even a .38-55 WCF lurking in your .375 Holland & Holland Magnum, and a .45-70 inside your mighty .458 Winchester Magnum!

The first question, of course, is "Why bother?" If you had wanted a
.300 Savage, you say, you'd have bought one in the first place, instead of
springing for a .300 Winchester Mag, right? Well and good. But think
back over the last year or so, and see just how many shots you've fired
with your thundering magnum. Five? Ten? Maybe a couple of boxes? If
you're like most shooters, your magnum hangs on the rack, reserved for
big-game season only, while you shoot something a little pleasanter and
more suitable for nonmagnum purposes—or *wish* you had something for
such shooting. Stairstepping the magnum down to lesser performance levels, through handloading, is at least one good answer to shooting more,
shooting more cheaply, and enjoying various sorts of sport for which full-
power magnum loads are stretching a good thing too far.

Such loading is very easy. Again, stay strictly away from the slow-
burning powders. Find charge weights which duplicate velocity levels of
the cartridge you're aiming to imitate by downward extrapolation. Of
course, any jacketed bullets may be used, but those used in the smaller
cartridge you're duplicating are most suitable unless a serious difference
in rifling twist rates appears. That's really all there is to stairstepping, besides the fact that you'll find you're enjoying your magnum rifle about
ten times as much as ever before and that your skill with it is growing by
leaps and bounds.

Handloading is the best and perhaps the only sure way to acclimate
a shooter to a magnum rifle's recoil, without risking development of a
serious flinch. Flinching is a completely involuntary effort on the part of
the subconscious mind to protect the shooter's body from pain or possible injury, and no amount of willpower can overcome a tendency to
flinch. The one and only way to avoid it is to convince the subconscious
that the rifle's recoil isn't going to hurt or harm you. And the best way to
accomplish that psychological selling job is to do a lot of shooting with
the magnum thunderstick, but only with very reduced loadings. First
trials should be with about half charges (one more time, do *not* reduce
slow-burning powder charges by more than 10 percent), and enough such
loads should be fired to become completely accustomed to the recoil.
When you find you don't even notice the kick, increase the powder
charge in your light loads by, say, 5 grains, and remain at that level for a
while. Then go up another 5 grains, and so forth. Somewhere in this process, it will be necessary to change back to the normal, slow-burning powder with which maximum velocities can be achieved, but by that time
you will probably have learned to deal with the recoil unconsciously. It is
possible to recoil-proof a youngster or a novice lady shooter in exactly the
same way, regardless of the cartridge. Let them shoot light loads year-

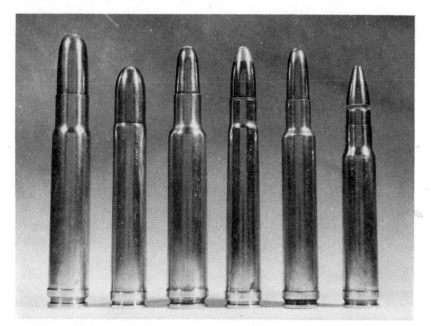

Here stand six good reasons for loading reduced-velocity ammunition; these are among the hardest kickers of today's popular big-game cartridges, and any shooter—no matter how hairy-chested—will enjoy practicing with such cartridges more with reduced loads. They are, from left, the .460 Weatherby, .458 Winchester, .378 Weatherby, .375 H&H, .340 Weatherby, and .358 Norma, Magnums all.

round to develop confidence and familiarity with the rifle, then put up some full-power hunting ammo, rezero the rifle yourself, and take them hunting. They will never notice the increased recoil, from then on.

Although most of the magnum revolvers can be fired with factory-built reduced loadings, the same thing can be accomplished with handloads. The mild .44 Special factory load works well in the .44 Magnum, and .38 Special commercial ammo in several different power levels can be used in a .357 Magnum. The .41 Magnum comes in two different loadings from the factory, one of which is a somewhat reduced load with a lead bullet. Factory rounds cost money, however, and there's no reason a reloader can't increase the flexibility of his big revolver in exactly the same way he extends his rifles' performance. Full-blown, "planet-wrecker" loads will eventually knock even the finest revolver out of time and produce unnecessary wear on its parts. For plinking, practice, small-game

Two different approaches to shot loads in a .38 or .357 Magnum revolver. At left is the commercially loaded Remco shot capsule which is seated like a bullet. At right are the components for the somewhat less expensive home-brewed load: two Hodgdon plastic shot cups and a charge of pellets. The assembly of the load is described in the text.

shooting, and recoil-proofing, mild handloads are not only easier on the shooter but easier on the gun, as well. Most loading manuals give a good selection of mild loadings for the big sixguns.

Unfortunately, semiautomatic handguns don't respond to reduced loads very readily, at least not if you wish them to function as semiautos. On the other hand, having to operate the slide of a pistol by hand for every shot isn't all bad; at least you don't have two-thirds of your precious fired brass flung into deep grass from which you can never recover it.

Another project for owners of revolvers is the loading of shot loads for same. The easy way is with the empty shot capsules sold by Speer for use in .38s and .44s, and with the prefilled Remco shot capsules in these and other calibers. Plastic capsules protect the shot from the rifling and deliver better patterns as a rule, but they are not essential to homebrewed shot loads. Hodgdon sells plastic cup wads for use in .38s for just this purpose. In the .357 Magnum, for example, one of these is seated, skirt up, over a charge of 4 grains of Hercules Green Dot powder (see Hodgdon's reloading manual for other loads) and about 86 grains of #9 pellets are poured in. Then another Hodgdon wad is seated, this one skirt down, flush with the mouth of the case, which is heavily crimped. Even home-made cardboard wads can be made to serve. The resulting loads are murderous against poisonous snakes, for example, at ranges of up to about 5

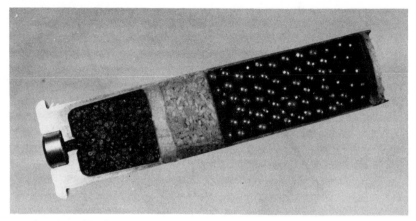

An example of a special loading easily assembled by a handloader but totally unavailable to shooters of factory ammo is this shot load for the .45-70 cartridge. Such loads are not suitable in bottle-necked rifle cases, however.

yards. If I had a dime for every rusty-backed old rattler I've stretched out with just such revolver shot loads during the last twenty years, I'd be rich.

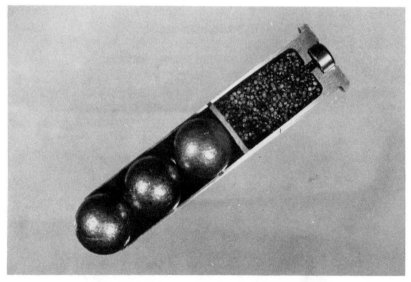

The author calls this his "hockshop" load for the .45-70, a fun loading featuring three soft lead balls at moderate velocity. Results are surprisingly good up to about 25 yards, with all three balls in a 2½-inch circle.

The only rifle cartridge in which I've ever developed satisfactory shot cartridges is the .45-70, using unprotected shot charges and cutting filler wads from sheet cork or fiber. Results were so-so, even more deadly than the pistol shotshells at short ranges, but without much additional range despite the greater number of pellets in the charge. If velocities are boosted much above 1,000 FPS, patterns become very patchy even at 10 yards, and I doubt that I will ever make my .45-70 a suitable quail gun. It is, however, death on sparrows and rats at short distances.

In the realm of special-purpose handloads, the sky's the limit. Most such loadings are working at low-to-medium pressure levels, which gives us more freedom to experiment than with maximum loads, and a little deep thought can devise a way to accomplish almost anything. This is the best area in which to get "creative" in your handloading, rather than with hot stuff which is crowding the limits of safety to begin with. Reduced loads inherently offer more elbow room in which to exercise your imagination, in addition to which the products are uniquely useful.

Handloaders who never put together anything but gut-busting maximum ammunition are missing some of the most fun and most interesting aspects of their hobby.

17

Wildcat Cartridges

Sooner or later, every handloader of metallic ammunition will hear the siren song of the wildcat cartridge. Most of us suspect that we can design a cartridge which will be better than anything the commercial ammo manufacturers have produced, and, even if it won't be *better*, it will at least be *ours*, something unique, a one-of-a-kind upon which our hope for reloading immortality may rest.

Such hopes are usually disappointed. Wildcat cartridges are rarely better than commercial rounds except for very specialized purposes, almost never unique, and about 95 percent of the thousands so far devised have proved all too mortal, along with their fond designers.

On the other hand, a few wildcat rifle and pistol cartridges, past and present, have turned out to be extremely useful. In many cases, they have had a profound influence on commercial ammunition development, and some have passed into commercial manufacture with little change. Today's wildcatter follows an honorable trail blazed by such early experimenters as Ned Roberts, Wotkyns, Ackley, Whelen, Sharps, and many other illustrious names. And who knows but what some real breakthrough in ballistic efficiency still remains to be discovered by a private experimenter?

Most case-forming for wildcats involves neck and shoulder alterations to standard cases. This sequence, producing .35 Whelen Improved brass from .30-06 cases, is more or less typical. From left, an untouched .30-06 case, a .30-06 with neck expanded to .40 caliber, an expanded case necked down to .35 caliber, a case which has been fire-formed (note sharpened shoulder), and a loaded .35 Whelen Improved round.

A wildcat cartridge can be defined as one for which commercially manufactured cases are not available. One trouble with this definition is that, as it stands, it must include a host of obsolete cartridges which once were manufactured but for which brass is either nonexistent or so scarce as to fall into the collectors'-item category today. The only difference between these rounds and true wildcats is that the wildcats have never had factory-produced guns chambered for them (there are a few scattered exceptions to this rule) while many old rifles are still floating around with chambers cut for the obsolete calibers. From the handloader's viewpoint, there is no difference; cases for either must be formed from some other kind or caliber brass which is still available.

Standard factory cartridges that are identical, or very closely similar, to long-popular wildcats are, from left: .280 Remington, .25-06 Remington, .257 Roberts, 6mm Remington, .243 WCF, .220 Swift, .22-250 Remington, .225 WCF, and .17 Remington.

Among the commercial cartridges which enjoyed a long-lived popularity as wildcats prior to their legitimization by Remington or Winchester are the .22-250 Remington, 6mm Remington, .243 WCF, .257 Roberts, .25-06 Remington, .280 Remington, 7mm Remington Magnum, and .308 and .350 Norma Magnums. These became standard factory cartridges with little or no change from their wildcat forms. Others, like the .17 Remington, .225 WCF, .264 Winchester Magnum, and several of the Weatherby Magnum series, were clearly inspired by wildcats but had their case dimensions altered somewhat, usually to simplify mass production. Although quite a few wildcat cartridges for handguns have been devised from time to time, only one that I can think of has become a standard factory item, and that is the .44 Auto Mag. Several others, such as the .30 and .35 Herrett wildcats, have factory guns chambered for them, the Thompson-Center Contender single-shot interchangeable-barrel pistol in both these cases. Other handgun wildcats which have achieved a measure of popularity are the .357/.45 ACP and the .357 Bain & Davis, on a necked-down .44 Magnum case.

The simplest form of wildcat is the so-called "improved" cartridge. Cartridges which have considerable body taper and long, sloping shoulders are candidates for such treatment. A new chamber is cut which has minimum taper and a sharp shoulder, but which will accept and properly headspace commercial ammunition, and factory cartridges are simply fired in the improved chamber. The brass is "blown out" to fit the new chamber by firing pressures, and comes out of the chamber with a more modern appearance and increased powder capacity. It can then be reloaded to higher performance than the original form. An advantage to an "improved" rifle is that, in a pinch, factory ammo can be used in it with safety and relatively small losses in velocity. The .257 Roberts cartridge is the classic example of one which benefits greatly from such "improvement." So do the .250 Savage, .25-35 WCF, .30-30, 7×57 Mauser, and even the .30-06, to greater or lesser degrees.

The next step upward is cutting a new chamber which not only reduces body taper and sharpens the shoulder of a bottle-necked case, but relocates the shoulder forward, shortening the neck and increasing powder capacity considerably. The Gibbs line of wildcats exemplifies this idea. Fire-forming cases for such cartridges is a bit tricky, since some means of headspacing the unimproved cartridge in the chamber is necessary. The safest method is to neck the case up to a caliber larger than the final version will be, and then run it part way into a sizing die of the correct caliber to produce a funny-looking double shoulder, the forward one of which makes the cartridge a crush-fit in the chamber. The case is then loaded with a three-quarters-throttle load and fired. If all goes well, it will

Steps in reforming .30-30 WCF brass to .30 Herrett cases are shown in order from left. First is the parent .30-30 case. The second case has had its shoulder set back in a special die to proper position. The third case has been trimmed to length and inside-neck-reamed. At right is a loaded .30 Herrett round.

come out of the chamber perfectly fire-formed to the new configuration. Case loss through split shoulders is quite high during fire-forming with some lots of brass.

By far the most common procedure in forming wildcat brass is necking-up or necking-down—expanding or reducing neck diameter to hold a bullet of a diameter different from that the original case held. The .22-250 and .25-06 Remington cartridges were created as wildcats during the 1920s and '30s, by necking the .250 Savage down to .22 caliber, and the .30-06 case down to .25 caliber, with no other changes. Another of the great wildcats of all time, the .35 Whelen, came about when a hand-loader simply enlarged the neck of the .30-06 to accept a .35 caliber bullet. The one and only wildcat cartridge which I can claim to have invented (chiefly, I suppose, because nobody else was willing to bother with such an oddball) is the .25-222 Copperhead, made by necking .222 Remington brass up to take .25 bullets. Two more of my favorites, the 6.5/284 and the .416 Taylor, are made by reducing the .284 WCF case neck to take .264-diameter slugs and the .458 Winchester Magnum case to hold .416-inch bullets. Far more wildcats, it may be noted, have arisen from necking-*down* operations than from necking-*up*. Most wildcatters are looking for higher velocities, and necking-down adds velocity potential, up to a point, while enlarging the bore diameter relative to case capacity increases efficiency but adds very little to velocities.

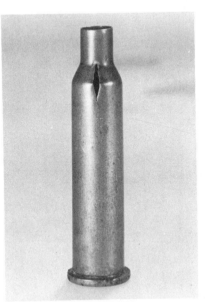

A rather typical case failure occurring during fire-forming. This is not the result of a reloading mistake, and little can be done about it. Certain lots of brass are prone to split shoulders and others are not.

Most wildcat cartridges require special case-forming dies. In addition to the regular resizing and bullet-seating dies on each side, this .17-223 wildcat requires a forming die and a file-trim die to convert standard .223 Remington or 5.56mm NATO brass.

This cartridge is the author's wildcat .25/222 Copperhead, shown with the variety of bullets for which it is adapted. At left are four cast bullets for squirrel, plinking, and practice loads, while at right are jacketed bullets weighing 100, 87, 75, and 60 (last two) grains, making the Copperhead an extraordinarily versatile cartridge for every sort of game smaller than whitetail deer.

There are other reasons than mere speed for wildcats, however, and it may be that today they are the most valid reasons for the trouble and expense of developing a nonstandard cartridge which requires custom-made chamber reamers, barrels, and reloading dies, among other things. Most of these reasons are mechanical. I built the aforementioned .25-222 Copperhead not because it would do anything some factory round couldn't do, but because it could do it in a type of rifle to which no similar factory cartridge was adapted. I wanted to drive the lighter .25 caliber bullets at velocities of 2,600 to about 3,000 FPS (while retaining good cast-bullet capabilities) in a modern, short-action, box-magazine turnbolt rifle. The game I had in mind for this little rifle was the entire range of pests and edible game up to about the size of the bobcat, coyote, and javelina, and especially wild turkey. I also wanted to be able to load cast bullets at squirrel-killing speeds and do it all without undue destruction of meat and pelts. The .256 Winchester Magnum could have done everything I wished—but that's a rimmed case and rimmed cases are a nuisance in box magazines. Since I planned to reload all ammo for the new rifle anyway, it was no more trouble to assemble .25/222 stuff than .256 Winchester Magnum cartridges.

The little Copperhead has been a very great success, performing exactly as I'd hoped—even better in many respects—and now has more than a dozen years of satisfactory shooting and hunting behind it. I have no illusions that it will elevate my name to the ranks of such great ballistic pioneers as Roberts, Niedner, and Wotkyns, but it's been a lot of fun. Which is not a bad reason for a wildcat, in itself.

The .416 Taylor is another great wildcat which exists for purely mechanical reasons. It is the .458 Winchester Magnum necked down slightly to take 400-grain, .41-caliber bullets at velocities around 2,400 FPS. It is strictly a rifle for the heaviest and most dangerous game in the world, and I have used it on such brutes as Cape buffalo and African lion. In other hands, it has given a good account of itself on elephant, as well. However good it may be, however, the .416 Taylor (named for its developer, gun writer Bob Chatfield-Taylor) exactly duplicates the performance of a 1911-vintage British cartridge called the .416 Rigby, so why bother? Well, the Rigby is an enormous cartridge which requires very expensive oversized rifle actions, and cartridges range up to about $4 *per round*. Even reloadable brass is rare and costly. The Taylor wildcat works in any .30-06-length bolt-action, which means a lighter rifle with a shorter bolt-throw (important when a lion is charging), and a cheaper rifle even when the cost of special gunsmithing is included. The ammunition uses

Many wildcat cartridges are designed for big game. From left: .505 Barnes Supreme (.460 Weatherby necked up); .416 Taylor (.458 Winchester Magnum necked up); .35 Whelen Improved; .30-.338 Magnum; and 6.5mm/.284 WCF.

cheap, easily available components, and has proved very tractable and efficient, so why not? In this case, the wildcat is simply more practical.

Many, perhaps most, benchrest competition rifles are chambered to wildcat cartridges. These are ultra-high-grade rifles anyway, and it's no more expensive to barrel one in a nonstandard cartridge than to a factory number. Benchresters are finicky about things, and are rarely satisfied with anything factory-built; their fondness for such wildcat cartridges as the .222½ Shilen arises from an effort to *exactly* match case capacity, brass design, and bullet diameter to the precise, optimum requirements of their demanding sport. What they seek is absolute perfection, and no factory cartridge (or wildcat, either, for that matter) is perfect. It's as simple as that.

The days when no American-made rifles were chambered to such calibers as 6mm, 6.5mm, 7mm, or high-performance .22s, .25s, .30s, or .35s were the heyday of the wildcatters. They could almost pick a caliber at random and work out a wildcat which would shade its commercial counterparts with ease. Since World War II, however, the picture has

Most wildcats today have some rather specialized purpose. These 7mm/ .300 Weatherby cartridges are used for ultraprecise target shooting at ranges up to 1,000 yards, but would offer no practical advantage for normal hunting purposes over standard 7mm Magnum chamberings.

changed, and it's difficult to find any spot in the lineup of calibers in which the factory-designed incumbent isn't already close to maximum performance levels. Today's wildcats, if they are to be of any value, must be designed for some fairly specialized purpose, one for which the general market is not likely to be inviting to a major manufacturer. There's still room for wildcats, but it's getting harder to find it.

Wildcat cartridges present the handloader with several problems other than the mechanical one of reforming brass. One is the fact that, except for a few very popular wildcats, there is little or no published reloading data available, at least from the same reliable sources from which we can pick loads for standard rounds. The articles written in shooting magazines about this or that wildcat, usually by its nonprofessional inventor, have tended to some pretty giddy claims. Velocities may have been produced as claimed, but little is said about pressures. Furthermore, since wildcat cartridges are, by definition, nonstandard, no standardized dimensional data on chambers and cases exist. Every wildcat rifle chamber is a law unto itself, and even sound data developed in other rifles or pistols may be dangerous in yours. In general, you're on your own in working up loads, and you're working without the benefit of the sophisticated laboratory equipment available to Remington and Winchester researchers. Wildcatting, then, can be seen as a venture in the wild blue yonder, and is best reserved for the mature, the cautious, and the experienced handloader.

This is not to discourage the ancient and almost uniquely American art of wildcatting. Far from it; wildcatting has contributed a great deal to the present-day richness of our shooting sports, and I hope it will continue to do so. There's a great deal to be found out about the efficiency of the small-capacity cases. There's work to be done in making varmint rifles quieter, as the population grows and expands into areas with woodchucks and jackrabbits. There's room for at least one more revolver cartridge, a long-cased, straight .25-caliber "magnum," and there may be room for more than one more auto pistol round. Who knows what else some ingenious wildcatter will turn up? Besides, wildcats are interesting,

A few small-game wildcats enjoying varying degrees of popularity are, from left: 6x47mm, .30 Herrett, .25/222 Copperhead (originated by the author), .17/223, .17 Mach IV, .22 Stark, and .25 Hornet. Factory-made guns have been chambered for the 6x47mm, .17/223, and .30 Herrett.

fun, and extremely informative, and if you can learn something more about your hobby from it, a wildcat project may be justified on that point alone. I remember the feeling which came over me one day when I realized, after more than a year and some hundreds of dollars spent developing a 6.5mm wildcat on the then-new .284 case, that I had succeeded in producing a cartridge which was not quite as good, all-round, as the .270 WCF, which had been around for almost fifty years!

Wildcats are expensive, and wildcat-chambered custom arms are not eminently salable, to put it mildly. You'll not likely recover any substantial portion of your investment when you decide to sell your super-duper, cab-over-engine .293 Jones Planet-Wrecker.

On the other hand, the very existence of the wildcat idea is a symbol of a treasured American freedom; most foreign governments would grow faint at the very thought of permitting their people to possess cartridge components, much less to invent their own calibers and build firearms around them. Even in free nations, a discussion of your latest wildcat will get you some uncomprehending stares from shooters. The idea just never occurred to them, as I well know from dealing with customs officials and safari staffs when I took my .416 Taylor to Africa.

On the whole, modern wildcatting may be less rewarding than it was during the 1920s, but it's still a lively game and a sort of postgraduate study in ballistics and handloading. Long may it live!

18

Cast Bullets

More game, large and small, and more men, good and bad, have undoubtedly been killed with plain lead bullets throughout history than with all the fancy jacketed slugs ever fired. That somewhat startling fact will very likely remain a fact, too, as long as .22 rimfire ammunition continues to be loaded with such bullets. Lead projectiles, usually cast, were the standard bullets for all firearms, including artillery, for the first 500 years of the history of gunpowder. Every major war from about 1700 until World War I in this century was fought entirely or largely with plain lead bullets. Every species of game on the face of the earth has been taken with cast bullets. Cast bullets wiped out the "numberless" American bison and wrote an end to the glory-days of the plains Indians. Every continent was conquered and colonized eventually with cast bullets. In short, such bullets made firearms possible and then made the improvements in them practical. Many cartridges besides rimfires are still loaded with plain lead bullets today, in the most modern ammunition factories.

Surprisingly, cast bullets for handloaders have achieved new technological sophistication within the last few years, which has pushed cast-bullet performance to levels far beyond those ever dreamed possible by our ancestors who knew no other kind of bullet. There is a sort of cast-bullet renaissance in progress today which has nothing to do with nos-

The stuff of which cast bullets are made is easily available and inexpensive. At lower left are bars of printers' Linotype metal, followed, clockwise, by muffin-tin pigs of alloy, gas checks, a cake of bullet lubricant, and an old candle for fluxing.

talgia; cast bullets are being shot for performance and economy, and perhaps because making one's own projectiles is the ultimate do-it-yourself step in reloading.

There is a good deal more to these unglamorous chunks of lead than meets the eye. The first consideration is that of the material of which they are made. For muzzle-loading firearms, they're usually of pure lead, but for all cartridge arms the lead is alloyed to some degree with other metals, most commonly tin and/or antimony. The specific alloy of which a bullet is cast affects its accuracy, its tendency to deposit lead in the bore of a rifle or pistol, its ease of casting and sizing, and its weight and diameter. Both antimony and tin increase the hardness and strength of cast bullets, and both also increase fluidity of the molten metal and produce sharper, better-filled-out bullets. Lead alloyed with antimony has less shrinkage in cooling in the mold, so such an alloy produces bullets of larger diameter in a given mold than does pure lead. The alloy, however, makes lighter bullets even though they're larger.

The critical factors in cast-bullet performance are strength, hardness, and diameter relative to the dimensions of the bore through which they will be fired. For very low-velocity loads in rifles or pistols (under 1,000 FPS), almost any alloy will work fairly well. As velocities increase, pressures and stresses on the bullet increase and the hardness of the alloy becomes important. The two most convenient sources of good, all-round bullet metal are used wheelweights (for balancing automobile tires) and printers' Linotype metal. The former are available, usually at no charge, wherever tires are balanced, and are usually 90 percent lead, 9 percent antimony, and 1 percent tin. Linotype can often be scrounged or purchased used from printing shops, and is made up of 84 percent lead, 12 percent antimony, and 4 percent tin. Make certain you get *Linotype* metal; stereotype and other alloys sometimes used by printers are largely useless. Linotype which has been remelted many times may have changed in its composition, becoming softer, so try to find out whether the metal you get is fairly new or oft-used. Linotype is so good a cast-bullet metal that I've used nothing else for many years except in my muzzle-loaders. However, ingenious handloaders scrounge bullet material from many sources, including lead pipe, lead cable sheating, plumber's wiped joints, plumber's lead, storage battery plates, Babbitt metals, salvaged bullets from range backstops, and many others. Some of these scrap-metal sources provide metal of uncertain alloy, and are hardly worth the trouble, although Saeco does make a bullet-hardness tester which may help the scrounger guess what sort of stuff he has.

I'd recommend Linotype for all rifle bullets, gas-checked or not, regardless of the intended velocity. For hot handgun loads, especially the magnums, nothing softer than 10 parts lead to 1 part each of antimony and tin is indicated. Moderate loads and midrange practice ammo can use a somewhat softer metal, say 40 parts lead to 1 part each of antimony and tin. For the battering bullets get in semiautomatic pistols, a 20-1-1 mixture is about as soft as can be expected to function properly.

Bullet molds are available in hundreds of different designs and calibers, from Lyman, RCBS, Hensley & Gibbs, Lee, Shiloh, Saeco, and other firms, and selection of a design poses a problem for the inexperienced caster. The problem can be reduced somewhat by observing a couple of rules. The first is, for general purposes, to choose a bullet in the upper half of the normal bullet-weight range in that caliber. For example, bullets considered normal for the .30-06 range in weight from about 110 to 220 grains, and good results may be expected of a cast bullet weighing about 160 grains and upward. The second rule is more important: always select a blunt-nosed design. Round- or flat-nosed cast bullets

Bullet molds are available for almost every conceivable bore diameter and purpose: Above the handle hinge is a mold casting a hollow-base Minié ball; at far right is a round-ball mold; under the hinge is a bevel-base wadcutter mold for target .38 loads; and the others are for various rifles and handguns.

Of these two different designs of bullets of the same weight and caliber, the flat-nosed pattern on the right will consistently outperform the spitzer.

are shorter than snouty spitzers, and therefore easier to stabilize in normal rifling twists at the moderate velocities most practical for cast-bullet shooting.

Such bullets are available in two basic styles, one with many narrow lubrication grooves, called "Loverin style," and the other with two or three wider, deeper grooves. The Loverin bullets are one uniform diameter on their bands from stem to stern, whereas the other type is most often of two different diameters, the nose section of correct diameter to ride on top of the rifling lands, with the intergroove bands on the shank of the bullet sized to fill the rifling grooves. Thus, for a .30 caliber rifle, such a bullet's nose section should mike .300", while the body measures .308", or a thousandth or two larger.

I've never had much luck with the so-called Loverin bullet in any caliber, although in certain bore sizes this has been the only type of bullet mold available in the right weights. The two-diameter bullet is by far the most satisfactory in modern use.

Very lightweight cast bullets for the caliber have their uses, for squib and squirrel loads, and for short-range gallery and plinking loads in which the very utmost economy is needed. But they should be treated as the special-purpose projectiles they are, and not loaded for all-round shooting.

The multigrooved Loverin-style bullet at right has not been as satisfactory in the author's experience as the so-called Keith type bullet illustrated at left, especially in loads which require one or more of the grease grooves to be seated outside the bullet neck.

Bullet casting need not be an elaborate process with expensive equipment; the few simple items shown here can produce good bullets for rifle or handgun. From left, a mold with handles attached, a lead dipper, a cast-iron melting pot, a hardwood mallet, a skimmer made from an old tablespoon, and homemade cake-cutters for pan-and-pour lubricating. Below the pot is shown a Lyman 310 tool with bullet-sizing chamber installed.

With a stock of suitable metal in hand and a good bullet mold chosen, the next matter is melting the lead alloy and preparing it for actual casting. This can be done in many ways, ranging from an inexpensive cast-iron pot on the kitchen stove to a thermostatically controlled electric melting pot especially designed for bullet molding. Good results can be had with either type of equipment and with any number of options in between. An ideal compromise is the cast-iron pot on a gasoline or propane portable camp stove. Casting bullets on the kitchen range produces good enough bullets, but the inevitable deterioration in family relationships probably isn't worth it.

I think I can produce a higher *percentage* of usable bullets with a pot and dipper, but I can cast them so much faster with a bottom-draw

An electric melting pot with bottom-draw spout greatly increases cast-bullet production rates.

electric pot that I get *more* good bullets in a similar period of time by that method, and that's the one I use.

Whichever you choose, the basic procedure is the same. Turn the heat up and add alloy to the pot. A few small pieces, such as imperfect bullets saved from the last casting session, speed up the melt. When the metal is completely molten, it will be seen to have a gray scum on the surface. If you skim this away without fluxing, you will be losing some of that precious antimony and tin and softening the alloy.

Fluxing merely means adding a lubricant to the molten metal. This can be paraffin, a chunk of candle wax, a nugget of beeswax or bullet lube, or one of the modern powdered fluxes used in printing foundries and by bullet-casters (one is trade named MARVELUX). They all work about equally well, differing principally in the quantity and obnoxiousness of the fumes given off when added to molten lead. As soon as the flux has liquefied, the alloy should be stirred vigorously, preferably from bottom to top with a dipper or wooden-handled tablespoon. The smoke created by the flux can be ignited to reduce vapors; it will burn merrily. The fluxing and stirring help to remix the various elements of the alloy, which tend to separate upon melting. Now, and only now, the slag

Fluxing molten lead alloy produces gases that can be ignited with a match to reduce odors and fumes. Stir the melt vigorously as long as the gases burn, and then—and only then—skim the dross from the surface.

can be skimmed off the melt, for which purpose the aforementioned wooden-handled tablespoon with a few holes drilled in the bowl is nothing less than perfect. Finally, the metal is ready for actual casting.

If the mold, fitted to its handles, is of ferrous metal (some are aluminum), it will probably have a coating of some sort of rust-resisting oil. This should be cleaned out before casting begins; it can be burned out by actual casting, but it takes a while and the residue may be undesirable. Denatured alcohol does a fair job of degreasing molds, but one of the aerosol degreasers sold in gunshops is quicker. In any case, the first bullets cast in a new mold will not be usable, because traces of the rust-inhibitor will remain despite your best efforts, and because the mold blocks will still be cold.

Management of temperature is one of the arts of bullet casting. Ideally, mold and alloy should be kept at a constant temperature; if either is too cool, the bullets will be wrinkled and poorly filled out. If they're too hot, the bullets will have a frosted appearance. A thermostatically controlled electric pot is good at keeping the melt within a fairly narrow range of temperature, and the mold's temperature can be controlled by adjusting the speed of casting and by developing a regular rhythm in the operations.

If the dipper-and-pot method is being used, fill the dipper from the bottom of the pot, place the spout against the filler hole in the sprue plate of the mold, which has been rolled 90 degrees to the horizontal position, and rotate both dipper and mold as a unit to the upright position so that lead can pour into the mold. Allow the mold cavity to fill and overflow slightly, and replace the dipper in the pot. Now watch the puddle of lead remaining atop the sprue cutter closely. As the freshly cast bullet "freezes" in the mold, you will see a distinct color change on the sprue, and a crystalline texture will appear at its exact center.

Now tap the sprue-cutter lightly with a hardwood mallet (I use a hickory hammer handle without the hammer) and knock the sprue into a

If a cast bullet fails to drop from the mold cavity, use a hardwood mallet to tap the hinge or the end of the handle; never use any part of the mold blocks themselves.

receptacle. Open the mold handles and allow the bullet to drop gently onto a soft surface (a folded towel is ideal). The hot bullet is still very soft, and can be damaged by striking a hard surface, including another bullet. Close the mold gently, push the sprue cutter back into position with your mallet, and repeat the process. Casting with a bottom draw pot is essentially the same except that no dipper is used.

I mentioned rhythm. Casting should be a rhythmic process, the rate of production varying according to the size of the bullets being cast. A 500-grain .458 mold gets hotter and cools off faster (because there's less metal in the blocks themselves) than a 50-grain .22 mold. The key is the time required for the sprue to harden properly. It should require a few seconds after the last molten lead is added, but if the sprue is knocked off too soon, a ragged hole will be torn in the base of the bullet and it will be ruined. Different molds perform quite differently. Some drop perfect bullets as soon as they're brought up to temperature and produce very few rejects, while other, apparently identical molds will never deliver more

Cast-bullet molds have distinct personalities. Once they are well broken in and delivering satisfactory bullets, care for them tenderly, and never loan them out. Here are a few of the author's cherished favorites in calibers from .25 to .45

than half their bullets in usable shape, no matter what you do to or with them. You have to get to know the characteristics of each individual mold and adjust your techniques and timing to suit them.

One more thing: a good mold is a rare and precious possession. Treat it tenderly, care for it as though for a jewel of great worth, and never, never lend it out!

Fluxing cannot be overdone. It should always be done when fresh metal is added to the melt to keep the level in the pot uniform, and, of course, always before skimming. Regular and thorough fluxing is one of the secrets of consistent cast-bullet quality, which in turn is one of the secrets of satisfactory cast-bullet shooting.

Another of those secrets is careful inspection of the finished product. Basic inspection is by eye, in a good light, looking for wrinkles, improperly formed bullets, flaws in bases, or base cavities or raised sprues. The former are due to striking off sprues before the metal has frozen, the latter from too-loose sprue-cutter plates. Bases are crucial to good shooting, and nothing less than perfect bases should be retained. In fact, casting *perfect* bullets is easy enough that a serious reloader need not settle for even minor imperfections. If real target-grade accuracy is the object, bullet inspection may extend to actual weighing of every bullet to detect lightweight specimens which probably have concealed internal air pockets.

The next step is sizing and/or lubricating; usually both operations, plus seating gas checks, are accomplished by a single stroke of a lubrisizing tool such as those offered by Lyman, RCBS, or Saeco. Sizing is necessary because of the tolerances built into bullet molds, most of which tend to drop bullets at least a couple of thousandths oversize. These must be reduced to correct diameter, which varies according to the individual barrel in which they are to be fired. Expert opinions vary, but, as in the case of so many other aspects of handloading, the rifle or pistol itself is the final authority. Personally, I favor bullets which exactly match the bore (that is, groove diameter), and prefer not to shoot cast slugs more than .001″ over that diameter. Others standardize at .001″ and accept .002″, but very few shooters get good results with bullets larger than .002″ over groove diameter.

Sizing, however, damages bullets, and excessive sizing ruins them. Modern sizing dies do a good job, but reducing bullet diameter more than about .002″ below original as-cast girth almost always produces inferior accuracy. These numbers rightly indicate that if your bullet mold drops bullets which mike more than about .004″ over the groove diameter of your rifle and top accuracy is your goal, you'd better get yourself another mold!

In the absence of a lubrisizer, cast bullets can be lubricated (but not re-sized) in this manner. The bullets are set on their bases in a pan and melted lubricant poured around them to the proper level. When the wax has cooled, the bullets are removed from the cake with a Lyman Kake-Kutter or a cartridge case with the head cut off and the neck expanded (lying on table at upper right).

This device lubricates, sizes, and gas-checks cast bullets with a single stroke of the lever.

Plain lead-alloy bullets, without jackets, must be lubricated to avoid rubbing hard-to-remove lead deposits off in the barrel. In the old days, bear grease and buffalo tallow had large followings, and would probably still work today. The search for the perfect cast-bullet lube has extended itself into every sort of substance known to man to be slick, and some of the secret formulae for bullet lubes read like something out of an alchemist's or wizard's notebook. The best thing found so far, however, is not only fairly simple but readily available. It is a mixture of pure beeswax and a synthetic substance known as Alox 2138F, in 50-50 proportions. The mixture is available in dozens of different brand names; just ask for "Alox lube" and you'll have one that's so good that further experimenting seems to be a waste of time. It is not too much to say that the discov-

The discovery of Alox as an ingredient in lubricants was a major development in cast-bullet technology. Most major brands include the magic stuff, and say so on the package.

ery of Alox 2138F, together with tapered sizing dies (the common kind, these days), has revolutionized cast-bullet shooting.

Gas checks are shallow gilding-metal cups which are fitted to the bases of cast bullets designed for them, to protect the soft metal from the tremendous heat of the powder gases. In general, any alloy bullet driven faster than about 1,600 FPS should have a gas check, to help prevent leading in the bore and to improve accuracy. If a bullet has the stepped heel for a gas check, use one; despite references in the literature to successful low-velocity use of gas-check-type bullets without their gas checks, I have never achieved anything better than peach-basket grouping with naked metal, at *any* velocity, if the design called for a gas check.

Two types of gas checks are marketed today, the standard type offered by Lyman and the so-called "crimp-on" type sold by Hornady. The latter are literally crimped into the soft alloy of the bullet when the combination is forced through a sizing die, the theory being that gas checks which are shed in flight destroy accuracy. There may be merit in this idea, but it's also true that very hard bullet metal such as Linotype resists the crimping action so determinedly that bullet and check may be deformed in the effort, and I have actually broken the handle of a lubri-sizer trying to crimp Hornady gas checks onto slightly oversized, hard bullets. Therefore, I use the crimp-ons when I can, and the noncrimping Lyman gas checks when I can't, depending upon the metal and design of the bullet itself.

With a goodly batch of gleaming new bullets cast, inspected, sized, lubricated, and, if necessary, gas-checked, we are ready to move on to an examination of the special techniques involved in assembling accurate ammunition around them. Obviously, if we place any sort of value on our time, cast bullets are not exactly free, even if we can scrounge all the materials which go into them. To be worth the effort, they'd better have something to offer besides economy . . . and they do, as we shall see.

19

Loading Cast Bullets

There are veteran handloaders who regard the loading of cast bullets as a sort of postgraduate exercise in the art of reloading, and there's something to be said for this viewpoint. Anyone can pick a jacketed-bullet load out of a handbook, follow the recipe, and wind up with ammunition which will deliver at least acceptable results in his rifle or handgun. Not so with cast bullets. They seem to require a certain cunning, in addition to technical expertise, that is not possessed by every handloader in the world.

Perhaps the word should be patience, instead of cunning. In any case, I have known reloaders who could make cast bullets do everything except deal poker hands while others, equally knowledgeable, never seem to have any "luck" with these fascinating chunks of lead.

Cast bullets have traditionally been for moderate- to low-velocity loadings, at least in rifles. Until recently, about 2,000 feet per second was taken as the general upper limit of cast-bullet velocities. This means, of course, that some of the older cartridges such as the .30-30 WCF or .35 Remington can be loaded to full *normal* velocities with cast bullets, but more modern rounds relegated cast-bullet loads to reduced-velocity status. This is not entirely true any longer. Alox-based lubricants, modern cast-bullet designs, and new loading techniques have unquestionably

Cast bullets are suitable for use in all centerfire calibers now popular (and many not so popular) except the .17s.

raised the practical velocity limits. Some experimenters have reported good results at velocities of 2,600, 2,800, and even 3,000 FPS, but other reloaders have been frustrated in trying to duplicate those results. A newcomer to the world of cast bullets is still well advised to keep his velocities to about 2,200 FPS and below, at least until he learns some of the tricks of the cast-bullet trade.

The reason for this is that the very strongest lead-alloy bullet is still relatively soft and weak compared to jacketed slugs, and is easily deformed by the heat and pressure of firing. The higher the velocity, the greater the heat and pressure, and the more deformation of the bullet, the wilder the shooting. It's *possible* to get good results with lead bullets at high velocities, but it sure isn't *easy*.

Most of the purposes for which home-cast slugs are used don't require high speeds anyhow. The majority of such loads are probably for plinking and practice shooting with a big-game rifle during the off season, and such shooting generally is done at 100 yards or less. Cast bullets are ideal: they're cheap, are easy on the barrel, and can have more than enough accuracy for these purposes. The second most common use is small game, for the pot or for pelts, and modest velocities are a must for this kind of hunting.

Cases for normal cast-bullet loads are prepared in exactly the same manner as for loading jacketed bullets, except that case mouths must be flared or belled slightly. If they are not, a soft lead bullet which is even slightly cocked during the seating process would catch the lip of the case and crumple it. Flaring has already been discussed in the chapter on die adjustments, but there is another way to accomplish it if one doesn't wish

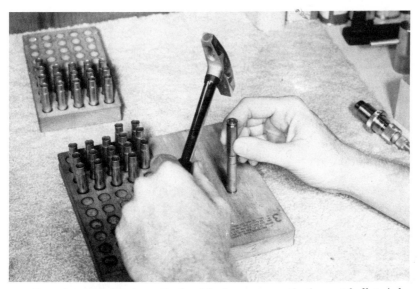

One of several simple methods of flaring case mouths for cast bullets is by tapping the shoulder of another case against the mouth. Here, a .308 WCF case is being used as a flaring tool for .35 Remingtons.

to invest in a special sizing die (dies for straight cases normally come with provisions for belling mouths, but those for bottle-necked cases ordinarily do not). It is done simply by tapping a bullet of considerably greater diameter nose-first into the case mouth. I use a .35 caliber bullet for everything up to caliber .30, and keep a full-jacketed .50 caliber machine-gun bullet on hand for everything larger. This must be done *before* the cases are primed, for obvious reasons. A little practice will teach you just how much tapping is required to flare the mouths the correct amount; overdo it and you cold-work the case mouths excessively and may have difficulty inserting them into the bullet-seating die.

Notes on powder selection for various cast-bullet and other low-velocity loadings are included in the chapter on special-purpose loads. Quite a bit of loading data is published for cast bullets, in a special handbook by Lyman, by Hodgdon, and in many popular shooting magazines, especially including *Handloader*. A few notes on primers may be helpful here. Since most of the powders used in reduced loadings are fairly easy to ignite, it might seem that primer selection would be no more critical in cast-bullet loads than in full-power loads with jacketed bullets, but this occasionally proves to be untrue. For reasons I cannot explain, now and then a reduced load turns out to be very finicky about primers. The phenomenon and its cure are both unpredictable, but it may be worth the trouble to substitute primer makes or types in a load which shows promise, as a part of the final fine-tuning of the formula. This is especially true if that load reveals a tendency toward vertical stringing of groups.

One of the major breakthroughs in cast-bullet performance in recent years has been the discovery of the effects of using a filler between the reduced powder charge and the base of the bullet. This is not really a new idea, having been developed decades ago when such inert materials as cornmeal or cream of wheat were used to fill the case after the powder charge was deposited. What's new about today's practices is the materials used and the systematic testing which has proved the value of such fillers quantitatively.

The original idea behind the use of fillers is still valid. It is that a small charge of powder in a large case will assume varying positions in the case, and varying shapes, from shot to shot. The primer flash may thus impinge upon a different surface area of powder and at a different angle

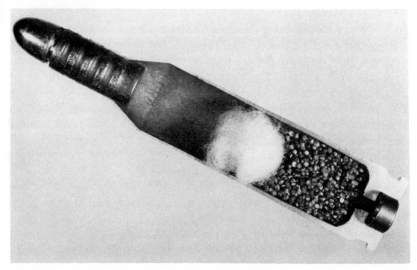

This cutaway round shows the purpose of Dacron or kapok in cast-bullet cartridges, holding the small powder charge in a uniform shape and position relative to the primer flash and insulating the base of the bullet from the hot gases of combustion.

from shot to shot, and variations in ignition can raise hob with ballistic uniformity. The filler, in the old days, was thought of as nothing more than a device to hold the powder charge in a uniform shape and uniform relationship to the primer. This is still a useful goal, but we now know that the filler serves another, perhaps more important, purpose, and that is to insulate the cast-bullet base from the heat of combustion.

We could still use cornmeal, but its weight must be added to that of the projectile in compounding loads since it is not consumed in firing. Experimenters a few years ago began working with kapok, a natural fiber, to lighten the total ejecta of the load, and got good results. Next, the synthetic fiber Dacron was tried, and this has now become standard among serious cast-bullet loaders. A buck or two will buy almost a lifetime supply of Dacron from most upholstery shops, since no more than 1½ grains is used in most loads even in the largest cartridges. One-half to 1 grain is more common in typical cast-bullet loads in rifle cases. Dacron is not used in handguns much, because normal powder charges usually fill most of the available case space.

The procedure is quite simple. After charging cases, the reloader plucks a tuft of Dacron from his supply, balls it lightly by rolling between his fingers, and stuffs it into the case, using a dowel to poke it firmly down atop the powder. In many cartridges, a pencil serves perfectly. For uniformity, it's a good idea to weigh each tuft of Dacron at first, but you will quickly develop the knack of plucking very close to the desired weight of fiber by eye and can discontinue the weighing step.

In cases up to the .308 in capacity, start with ½ grain of Dacron. In .222-sized cases and smaller, ½ grain will be about maximum. In .30-06 and larger cartridges, the right amount will usually be found between 1 and 1½ grains in most loads. Not surprisingly, shooting in hot weather may require more Dacron than the same load needs on cool days. Only personal experimenting with your own rifle can reveal the just-right loading. Careful group-shooting should show distinctly smaller spreads as well as rounder groups (without marked stringing tendencies, either horizontal or vertical) with Dacron if the load is accurate enough to make such distinctions to begin with.

Cast bullets are seated in the same manner as their jacketed counterparts, but care should be taken to see that the seating punch in your die does not deform the bullet's nose. If you don't happen to have the correct punch on hand, improvise. The right shape can be built into the existing punch with sealing wax or epoxy putty, using a cast bullet as a mold to form the material before it hardens. The results should give good service, and can be removed any time you wish by the application of heat.

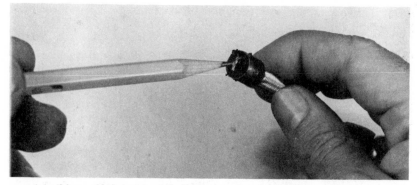

A build-up of lubricant on the bullet-seating screw while seating cast bullets can result in seating the bullets progressively more deeply. Watch for this and keep the seating screw clean to avoid trouble.

Excess lubricant on cast bullets may be squeezed or cut away from the sides of the bullets in seating, and tends to build up on the face of the seating punch. If allowed to continue, this process results in successive bullets being seated deeper and deeper. Watch closely for this development in loading a large lot of cast-bullet ammunition, and clean the face of the punch occasionally if it's observed.

Watch also for thin rings of lead being shaved from the bullets as they're forced into the case necks. Chamfering and flaring the mouths should prevent this, but since cast bullets are often sized a thousandth of an inch or two larger than jacketed bullets in the same caliber, the meticulous handloader may wish to get a special expander button for his case-sizing die for use in cast-bullet loads, to avoid squeezing his slugs down in the process of seating them in too tight case necks. Many manufacturers of reloading dies can furnish such oversize expanders on special order.

Wherever possible, cast bullets will give best results in uncrimped cases, and crimping is to be avoided except in heavy magnum revolver loads, when the ammunition will be subject to rough handling, and similar circumstances. The flare can be removed from the case mouths as described in the chapter on die adjustments.

Remember, too, the warning about using cases which have been fired with squib loads for full-power loadings in the future. Don't do it.

The "secret" to cast-bullet success, it should be obvious now, is in the delivery of perfect bullets at the muzzle. Careful casting of metal of the proper hardness, meticulous inspecting and rejection of all except perfect bullets, minimum sizing, protection of the metal from deformation

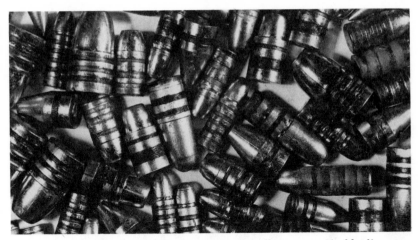

Bullet molds are available today casting virtually any conceivable diameter, weight, or shape of bullet for pistols or rifles.

by heat and pressure in firing, and adequate lubrication add up to good shooting, and it can be very good indeed. In fact, there's no particular reason that a rifle shouldn't shoot cast bullets as well as or better than jacketed slugs, and many cast-bullet shooters are disappointed with groups which exceed a minute of angle at 100 yards or even farther.

These comments must be qualified by caliber, for the reason that the smaller the bullet in mass and diameter, the more crucial very minor, almost imperceptible, flaws become. I have never achieved really top performance from .22 caliber cast bullets, and only rarely with 6mms. Conversely, 7mm and caliber .30 slugs have given beautiful results, and .35 and larger ones even finer accuracy.

Another factor which is often ignored is that cast bullets are very sensitive to barrel fouling from firing jacketed slugs. If you've been blazing away with the latter, take time to thoroughly clean your bore before switching to cast bullets. The difference in grouping may amaze you. Incidentally, the reverse is also true: jacketed bullets will not group well from a barrel in which a great many cast bullets have been fired, at least not for the first few rounds. Eventually, the high-velocity jacketed bullets will clean the cast-bullet fouling from the bore themselves. This is also the easiest way to clean a bore which has been leaded by driving cast bullets through it which were too soft, too fast, or insufficiently lubricated. If the bore is very heavily leaded, firing a high-velocity jacketed slug through

Careful selection of a cast-bullet style permits use in several cartridges of the same caliber. Here, the Lyman #257312 is shown alone, and loaded in .25-20 WCF, .250-3000 Savage, .257 Roberts, and .25-06 Remington cases.

it may produce dangerous pressures, but if only a minor deposit of lead is present a couple of full-power jacketed bullets will eliminate it.

Cast bullets are a challenge; no doubt about it. They require more know-how, more patience, and more effort for good results than jacketed bullets, which, for some, is the same as saying "Why bother?" But he who asks that question has never known the feeling of driving home the fifth shot in a 1-inch group with bullets he molded himself and observing the expression on the face of the shooter at the next bench who can't seem to do better than 2 inches with the finest modern jacketed slugs.

20

Loading for Black-Powder Guns

Sooner or later, almost every handloader either acquires an old black-powder breechloading rifle, or some friend asks him to help in providing ammunition for one. In most cases, handloading is the only hope for restoring these old-time smokepoles to service because factory ammunition is not available except in collectors' quantities and at collectors' prices.

The first problem is always cases. A couple of years ago a friend brought me a magnificent old Winchester Model 1886 rifle chambered for the .40-65 WCF cartridge, vintage of 1887. He had the original bullet mold and hand-type reloading tools, both marked "Winchester Repeating Arms Co.," and a couple of boxes of original factory ammunition. He wanted to shoot the old buffalo-killer, but he was aware of its considerable value on the collectors' market, and consulted me to make certain that nothing he did might damage the gun.

A quick check in Frank Barnes's *Cartridges of the World*, an invaluable reference in such matters, revealed that .40-65 WCF ammo had been discontinued by the manufacturers in 1935, so the cartridges my friend had couldn't have been younger than that. This posed the possibility that the primers in that ammunition were mercuric and corrosive; therefore, we decided not to run the risk of firing the factory loads. If there had been no other choice, we could have broken down those car-

Factory-loaded ammunition for black-powder cartridges should be treated with caution. Primers may be corrosive and mercuric, and firing this original ammo can result in corrosion damage to the barrel of a fine old gun and destruction of the cases by mercury residues. It's safest to deprime and reload old ammo with modern components.

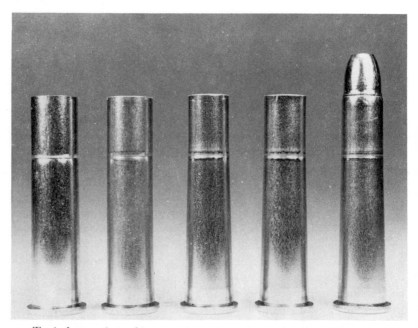

Typical steps in making new brass for reloading old rifles, this sequence shows how new .45-70 Government cases can be converted to .40-65 WCF. At left is a .45-70, followed by one after a pass through a forming die made for the purpose. The middle case has been run through a normal .40-65 sizing die, after which it is expanded and flared. At right, a loaded .40-65 cartridge. Most such conversions are just as easy.

tridges, salvaging bullets and cases and discarding powder and primers, and reloading the cases. As it happened however, we did have a choice, since modern .45-70 brass can be easily reformed to fit the .40-65 WCF chamber. Accordingly, we disassembled a couple of rounds to double-check correct bullet diameter (there were several common in the many early caliber .40 cartridges) and to satisfy our curiosity about the loads. These proved to be black powder.

While waiting for a set of RCBS loading dies in this caliber, I molded a number of bullets in the original mold which came with the rifle, and a few more in Lyman's #403196 mold. The latter weighed 260 grains in Linotype, while the same metal came out of the old mold weighing 235 grains. All were sized .406 inch.

When the dies arrived, I sized a few brand-new .45-70 cases in them and tried them in the rifle, finding that they would not quite chamber. The bases were not being squeezed down quite small enough due to interference between the shell-holder and the face of the die. Consultation with RCBS produced a sizing die for the similar, but longer, .40-82 WCF cartridge. The .45-70 cases were then driven into this die with a bench vise (properly lubed, of course) and knocked out with a steel punch. This technique sized the cases all the way to the rim and produced .40-65 cases which worked perfectly in the old rifle. From that point on, we were home free, having only to select a powder and charge. I even discovered that jacketed bullets in the correct diameter were available from Colorado Custom Bullets or from A. F. Sailer, of Owen, Wisconsin. The original ballistics of this cartridge called for a 260-grain bullet moving 1,325 FPS at the muzzle, and this was easily duplicated with 26 grains of IMR 4198 powder. Since this old Winchester has an extremely strong action and was in almost new condition, we cautiously experimented with heavier loads, successfully—and safely—achieving just under 2,000 FPS with the 250-grain jacketed Colorado Custom bullet. This rifle would make an effective and interesting arm for whitetail deer at normal ranges, or even for the bigger game it was originally designed for, if the owner cared to risk damage to the finish. The whole project was great fun, and a fine old rifle was allowed to roar again, after more than half a century of silence.

In that story are inherent several important points in load development for black-powder arms. First, make certain of the mechanical condition of the weapon, preferably by having it inspected by a competent gunsmith. Second, watch out for obsolete factory ammunition. If mercuric, corrosive primers are fired, the brass cases are hopelessly ruined, and the rifle will be damaged unless meticulously cleaned immediately after firing. If the ammunition is loaded with black powder, cleaning is all the

Reloading dies are available for virtually any centerfire cartridge ever designed, including obscure obsolete, foreign, or military rounds. The die standing outside the box is a special one for reforming modern .45-70 brass to fit the .40-65 WCF chamber.

more necessary. Furthermore, the primers may be deteriorated, and the cases themselves are probably not as strong as new ones. Wherever possible, it's worth the trouble to make new ones from current brass. More about this below.

If the cartridge in question is British or European, the primers are probably Berdan. If you attempt to deprime such cases in the conventional manner, you'll break your decapping pin and may damage your die. In some cases, it will be possible to make up reformed cases to fit the old gun from American brass with Boxer-type primer pockets, which saves an enormous amount of nuisance in future reloading. RCBS offers a tool for decapping Berdan-primed cases which is about the most satisfactory item for handling this job, but it's still a nuisance. Furthermore, it cannot be used to remove live primers. This can best be accomplished by removing the depriming stem from your resizing die and running the unloaded case all the way into the die. Then turn a steel rod to a sliding fit in the case neck. Fill each case with water, insert the rod, and administer a whack on the rod with a large hammer. Theoretically, hydraulic force will force out the primer. It will also spew water all over everything in sight, but it's the only safe way to decap live Berdan primers.

If no Boxer-type case can be converted to fit your Berdan-primed cartridge, you're stuck with using the latter primers, which are available although scarce on today's market. In that case, you'll need the RCBS tool for removing fired primers.

The sure way to pick a powder charge for a black-powder cartridge is to use black powder, which is also scarce but available in most areas. Use FFg granulation in a quantity which fills the case to the base of the bullet or a little above, so that seating the bullet will compress the powder charge about 1/8th inch. Having arrived at this charge volumetrically,

Greatly enlarged, black powder appears to form irregular chunks, in contrast to the regular shapes of smokeless powders.

you can then set your powder measure to drop this quantity without worry about charge *weight*. Personally, I don't care much for using a rotary powder measure with black powder; the stuff can be set off by static electricity and, conceivably, by the mechanical action of the measure. I know reloaders who get away with measuring powder this way, however, and have never heard of such an accident. I still prefer to use a dipper. Lee offers a graduated set of powder dippers which are quite handy, or you can make your own by soldering a wire handle to an old case which has been trimmed to hold the desired volume of black powder.

In some of the very small black-powder cartridges, the same procedure can be used, but the finer FFFg granulation substituted.

If the gun is in sound mechanical condition, this method of arriving at a propellant charge should give very similar pressures and velocities to original ammo, with points of impact which coincide with the factory sights on the guns, some of which are not adjustable. However, continued use of black powder in any gun will almost inevitably result in some deterioration of the bore and finish unless you're willing to spend an ungodly amount of time in cleaning after every firing. This involves washing the bore out with hot soapy water and the use of any of the newly developed black-powder solvents (thanks be to the muzzle-loaders!) on all parts of the action, inside and outside, followed by thorough oiling with corrosion-inhibiting lubricants, plus occasional inspection for a few days after each firing, just to be on the safe side.

If all that sounds a bit laborious, the solution is the use of smokeless powder, and that brings about a whole new set of problems. The principal one is pressure, specifically pressures beyond the capacity of obsolete actions to deal with them. This is complicated by the fact that different models from the black-powder era which were chambered for the same cartridge are of radically different strengths. A .45-70 load, for example, which is perfectly safe in an 1886 Winchester lever-action is quite likely to convert an 1873 trap-door Springfield's receiver to shrapnel on first firing!

Therefore, I'd recommend that reloaders wishing to develop smoke-less loads confine their activities to the aforementioned Winchester 1886 (and later lever actions) and 1885 single-shot "High Wall," the Sharps 1878 (Borchardt), the Marlin Models 1893, 1894, and 1895, the big Mar-tini actions, the Stevens 44½, and the Remington-Hepburn and similar rifles, assuming breeching, headspace, and firing pins are perfect. All other original black-powder arms are best fired with black powder only, includ-ing the old Colts, Bullards, Wessons, Maynards, rolling blocks, Whitneys, Ballards, Sharpses, and the Stevens, Winchester, and Marlin arms not on the above list. I concede that some of these *can* be fired with light charges of smokeless, but I consider the risk of doing so less desirable than the work of cleaning up after a black-powder-burning session.

There are several excellent sources of information on loads for the old cartridges, including the aforementioned Barnes book, *Cartridges of the World*, a large-format, softcover volume which is essential to any re-loading program with any obsolete or foreign cartridges. Another is Major George Nonte's hardback *Home Guide to Cartridge Conversions* (Stack-pole, 1961), which will be mentioned again. Also, *Handloader* magazine (bimonthly) and *Handloaders Digest* (annual) publish some loading data for black-powder cartridges.

It should be borne in mind that the steels in use during the black-powder days were by no means as sophisticated as those in modern guns. Some of the old barrels are relatively soft, and may be worn out quite rapidly by driving jacketed bullets through them at high velocities (for those cartridges). For this reason, cast bullets should be used for most shooting in the old guns, and powder charges kept below maximum to re-duce throat erosion from hot gases as much as possible. For most pur-poses, the cast bullets will do anything of which the cartridges are ca-pable, anyway. Furthermore, bore diameters varied quite a bit more before the turn of the century than today, and the handloader's ability to size cast bullets to almost any desired diameter may produce better re-sults with lead-alloy bullets than with jacketed ones. The bore size can be determined by slugging the bore of the rifle in question, driving a soft, *pure* lead ball a bit larger than the bore through it, carefully, and measur-

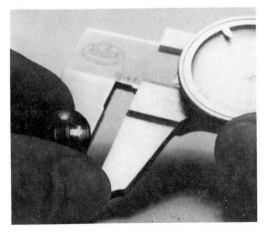

Slugging the bore of an old rifle (by pushing a soft lead ball through it) is the only sure way to determine proper bullet diameter.

ing the largest diameter of the slug with a micrometer. Very worn bores often do their best work with slightly oversize bullets, sometimes as much as .002″ over groove diameter.

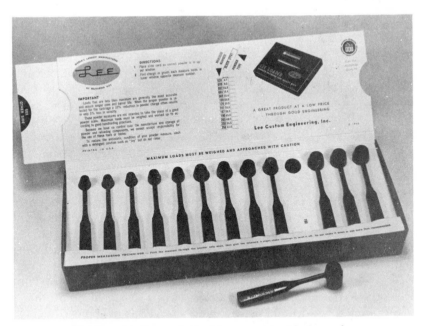

A set of Lee powder dippers is ideal for measuring black powder.

This RCBS .45 BASIC brass is a big, rimmed case from which more than twenty different obsolete or hard-to-find cases may be formed.

The description of my efforts to restore my friend's .40-65 WCF Winchester to service included some of the problems arising from trying to find shootable, reloadable brass for an obsolete caliber. For most handloaders, simple reforming and trimming to a new length, plus a bit of inside neck reaming and fire-forming, constitute the limit to which they'll go in manufacturing cases for black-powder rifles. It's amazing how many of the most popular old buffalo-busters can be made from the .45-70, .348 WCF, .30-40 Krag, and 9.3×74R cases, all of which are available with Boxer priming. RCBS offers what is called the "RCBS Basic" case, a big, rimmed .45 caliber case from which almost two dozen common and not-so-common black-powder cartridges can be formed, and Dixie Gun Works sells newly manufactured .50-70 brass. With this assortment available over the counter, most of the more esoteric conversions described in Nonte's *Home Guide to Cartridge Conversions* are not so necessary these days, but, just in case you need to know how to build up a Maynard case, that astounding book will tell you. It's a fundamental reference for handloaders who play with black-powder rifles.

Perhaps a few words on storage and handling of black powder here will save someone an unfortunate experience. I advise against storage of black powder in the home, and especially near any other combustibles. "Black" can be ignited, as mentioned, by an electric spark (including static electricity), heat, percussion, and fire. Unlike smokeless, it is officially classed as an explosive, and it need *not* be confined to burn violently. Keep stored quantities small, keep it separated from primers and smokeless powder and preferably in a magazine of approved design, and handle it cautiously. Black powder is far less forgiving than smoke-

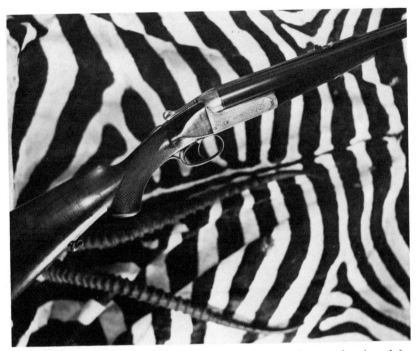

Many fine old English double-barreled big-game rifles are chambered for cartridges originally loaded with black powder. Although satisfactory smokeless powder loads may be possible in some of them, regulation of the points of impact of the two barrels with the sights may be difficult or even impossible.

less, and can never be taken for granted. When handling it, one must be *thinking* at all times. For example, it's best not to use a plastic funnel to transfer black powder between two containers, because common polyethylene funnels can build up static charges; use a metal one, preferably brass. Ferrous metal, which can cause a spark if struck sharply, should be avoided around black powder; remember, that's how a flintlock rifle ignites the stuff. With the exception of the containers in which black powder is sold, it has traditionally been stored in horn, brass, or copper, and with good reason.

It should go without saying that being wetted destroys black powder, unlike most smokeless, and that it's highly hygroscopic, and can pick up moisture from humid air. "Keep your powder dry" is still good advice where black powder is concerned, and that means storing it in a relatively cool, dry place.

Many old-time rifles have fixed sights, having been regulated at the factory for what was probably the only loading available in commercial ammunition. Today's black powders are not exactly the same as the ones in use in the 1880s, despite carrying the same granulation designations. This means that, unless a shooter wishes to alter his original black-powder rifle by adding adjustable sights (which may considerably reduce the value of the piece), he'll have to experiment with powder charges to try to find a load which strikes where the sights look at some useful distance. This can be a particular problem with the old British double-barreled rifles, in which there is not only a question of zeroing but one of trying to make both barrels shoot to the *same* zero. This can be a maddening procedure with smokeless powder, but can usually be achieved with a little experimenting with black powder. Unfortunately, there is no easy way around it; you just have to try everything you can think of until something works. Varying bullet weights may help.

In any case, many reloaders consider loading for the old-timers to be one of the most rewarding aspects of their hobby. There is an aura about the guns which fought the Civil War, wiped out the buffalo, and subdued the Apache, Sioux, and Arapahoe that's well nigh irresistible to any dyed-in-the-wool gun buff. These rifles spanned the brief period between the end of the muzzle-loading era and the coming of smokeless powder. They're a part of our history and a part of our shooting heritage—and they're one of the most satisfying parts of the handloading hobby.

21

Loading for Pistols and Revolvers

From the handloader's point of view, most handgun ammo falls into one of three major categories: hunting loads (mostly for revolvers), target loads (mostly for semiautomatics), and defense loads (may be for either type of handgun). Each of these categories has its own specialized requirements. Let's examine them separately.

Handguns used for hunting are usually revolvers, either single- or double-action, and usually chambered for one of the magnum cartridges, .357, .41, or .44, with the Ruger Blackhawk .45 Long Colt thrown in for good measure. The exceptions to these rules are the mighty Auto Mag autoloaders chambered for the .357 and .44 AMP cartridges, and, of course, .22 rimfire handguns of either persuasion used for pests and rabbit-size game.

The principal concern of the handgun hunter of big game is enough velocity to expand the jacketed bullets which he usually loads. Regardless of the brand or weight of bullets selected (typically hollow-points), velocities which exceed 1,000 FPS and 1,200 FPS or more will produce much more dependable expansion. In 4- to 5-inch barrels, such speeds are not as easily come by as a glance at the reloading manuals might suggest. Such loads are always close to permissible maximum chamber pressures, which calls for care in charging, seating bullets, and crimping. Top-quality brass

A lightweight, jacketed, hollowpoint bullet from the author's .357 Magnum Ruger did in this big coyote which came within seven yards in response to a predator call.

is a requisite, and that means *new* brass in the .44 Special and .45 Long Colt. Very old cases in either caliber may be found to be of the folded-head or balloon-head types. Avoid them for hunting loads.

There seems to be a modern trend to lighter bullets at high velocities for hunting, the idea being to produce flatter trajectories and enough energy to make bullets open up. Everyone to his own tastes, but I know quite a few pistoleros who have gone that route and then come back to the heavier slugs. I'm one of them. One hundred yards is long range for most of us on live game, and anybody who isn't sufficiently familiar with his trajectory to hit at such distances with any load has no business shooting at an animal which bleeds and feels pain. Therefore, my recommendation is a jacketed bullet with a lot of lead exposed in the upper 10 percent of the weight range for the caliber: Specifically, a bullet of at least 140 grains in the .357, 200 grains in the .41 Maggie, and 225 grains in the

Hollow-point bullets, like these in .45, .44, .38, and 9mm calibers, are currently in vogue for hunting and defense loads in handguns.

.44 Special, .44 Magnum, and .45 Colt. Of the five, the .357 Magnum is a little shaky as a hunting round, at best, and needs maximum penetration for effectiveness.

Handloading can greatly extend the versatility of almost any revolver. Shown here are seven different reloads for the .357 Magnum. From left: two shot loads, one with Hodgdon shot cups and the other with a Remco capsule, a low-velocity target load using a plain-base cast bullet, a maximum-effort defense load with the 148-grain hollow-base wadcutter reversed, a small-game and varmint load with a 110-grain jacketed HP, a heavy hunting load with 158-grain jacketed semi-wadcutter, and a heavy-bullet load featuring a 200-grain round-nosed lead slug.

All these cartridges need a heavy crimp in hunting loads, for optimum combustion of the very slow-burning powders and to prevent the bullets in the unfired chambers from being pulled through inertia under heavy recoil. If this happens, a bullet may protrude from the front of the chamber enough to prevent the cylinder's rotation, which puts the gun out of action. This could result in the escape of a wounded animal, and no sportsman risks that tragedy if the remedy is within his power.

In the .41 and fatter calibers, cast bullets actually work just about as well as jacketed ones. A .44 or .45 caliber slug cuts a fair-size hole even if it doesn't expand at all, and Linotype (or harder) cast bullets will not expand much at feasible velocities in these cartridges. Bullets of at least Linotype's strength and hardness, however, are required for accuracy and to prevent leading in the bore. Such slugs give deep penetration and maximum energy delivery in the vitals; the rest depends upon the marksmanship of the handgun hunter.

Target-handgun competitors have no choice but to reload, unless they were born rich, simply because mastery of the pistol requires so much practice that the price of factory loads virtually precludes the acquisition of championship skills. Practically all serious target shooting is done with two calibers, the .38 Special and the .45 ACP, and, these days, the majority of it is done with autoloading pistols.

The competitor is, of course, concerned with accuracy, first and foremost, although mechanical reliability is certainly not unimportant in a match where a malfunction means losing. Handloading ammo which equals the accuracy of industry-loaded match cartridges is not easy. In fact, the goal in such handloading is merely to *equal* factory stuff, and it's likely that most such handloads fail to do so. Serious accuracy testing requires the use of a return-to-battery mechanical rest for the gun, such as the Ransom or Lee models, to sift the human factor out of the testing, and relatively few reloaders invest in such equipment. Without it, you'll never really be sure of the quality of your loads.

In pistol ammo even more than in rifles, quality results from application of the most painstaking efforts toward absolute uniformity from round to round in the ammunition. As usual, everything begins with good bullets, and since these are usually cast by the reloader, extra care in fluxing, temperature control, casting technique, bullet inspection, lubrication, and sizing is mandatory. Bullet styles are important; most target bullets are either full- or semi-wadcutters, and the hollow-based designs are more difficult when trying to cast target-quality projectiles. Since feeding in autos is involved, the metal must be hard—at least as hard as Linotype to avoid deformation when driven against the feed ramp. Uni-

Compared to a factory .22 rimfire shot cartridge are products with which the handloader can assemble more efficient handgun shot cartridges. First is a .38 caliber Remco capsule, pre-filled with #9 pellets. Next is a Speer .38 capsule that can be filled with any size shot, and a loaded .38 Special round with the Speer device. At right is a Thompson-Center "Hotshot" .44 capsule (pre-filled) and a .44 Magnum round loaded for use in the long-chambered "Contender" pistol.

form bullet weight is much more important than exact weight; if you weigh all cast bullets and segregate them into groups which vary by ½ grain in average weight, you'll probably discover that both groups shoot about equally well but that they shoot to measurably different points of impact. Many match-winning handloaders hold the weight range within any one lot of cast bullets to plus or minus .1 or .15 grain.

Cases must be the best you have, for match purposes, carefully sorted, all of the same lot and age (if possible), trimmed to identical length. Primers should be all of the same manufacturing lot.

Many powders are used in match .38 and .45 loads, including several so-called shotgun powders, Norma's 1010, Hercules Unique, and others, but Hercules Bullseye still seems to win most of the matches. Charges are very light to reduce recoil and bullet deformation. Depending upon the particular gun, from 2.7 to 3.0 grains of Bullseye are common for the .38 Special with the wadcutter bullets of about 150 grains, and 3.0 to 3.5 grains are used behind typical target bullets in .45 ACP. The determining factor is the pistol itself; use as little powder as needed to work the action, provided accuracy remains good.

The .38s are best crimped lightly to keep the bullet from being driven back into the case when it rams against the feed ramp. Since the .45 headspaces on the case mouth, it cannot be crimped in the usual manner, which rolls the case lip into a groove on the bullet. A long taper crimp is preferable if bullets show a tendency to be seated deeper during feeding. A better idea, if it will work, is reducing the diameter of the expander button in the die so that case mouths have a tighter grip on the bullet. If overdone, however, such cases can squeeze bullets down too much even when the mouth is properly flared before seating bullets. Obviously, a fairly delicate adjustment between various factors is required here, with some experimenting necessary with the individual gun. A sort of last-resort possibility is rolling a cannelure deeply into the case at the point at which the bullet's base should rest. Perhaps a combination of techniques will best solve the problem.

Even though the .45 target loads will not be roll-crimped, cases must be of uniform length, again because of the headspacing system in these pistols. Short cases can cause weak ignition, and long ones can tie up the pistol. Yet .45 cases may not be trimmed much below normal length in an effort to make them uniform because excess headspace can result. Best bet is careful sorting of cases within a large lot of empties, to find enough which are the same length for loading match ammo.

On the whole, loading competition-grade handloads for target pistols is a tall order, but so many of today's finest target shooters succeed at it that it must not be impossible.

Loading for handguns to be used for self-defense and home defense is quite a different story. Any of dozens of different cartridges may be involved, and any of hundreds of models of guns of widely varying quality and characteristics. Probably the most common revolver rounds are the .32, .38, .357 Magnum, .41 Magnum, .44 Special, and .44 Magnum, while the pet autoloader rounds are the .32 ACP, .380, 9mm Luger, .38 Super, and .45 ACP. Since your life may hang upon it, unfailing mechanical functioning is paramount; everything—literally *everything*—else is subordinate to this requirement. The gun must not fail to fire each and every time the trigger is pulled as long as ammunition remains in clip or cylinder.

In sixguns (a few are *fiveguns* these days), this means careful case preparation and super-careful priming, making certain no lubricant reaches the primer pellets and that all primers are correctly bottomed in their pockets but not crushed. Bullets are carefully crimped in place, for the same reasons that hunting loads are.

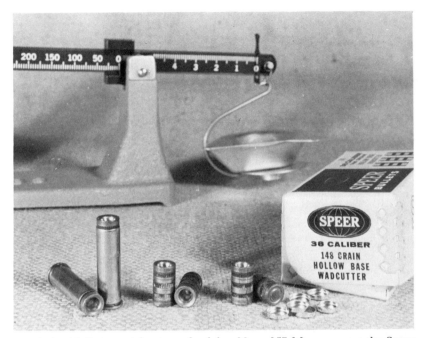

A devastating special-purpose load for .38 or .357 Magnum uses the Speer 148-grain hollow-base wadcutter target bullet seated backward so that the base cavity becomes a huge hollow-point. The wadcutter noses have Lyman gas checks seated on them so that the bullets can be given maximum velocity. Expansion is violent and penetration limited—an excellent defense load.

Bullet selection is according to different criteria, however. Most encounters in which this ammunition will be fired are at pointblank range, and too much penetration (on either hits or misses) may endanger innocent persons elsewhere in the house or vicinity. This, then, is the place for the lighter bullets in each caliber, and, I think, the place for hollowpoints at maximum velocities. Some authorities differ; this is my own opinion and my practice. Remember, these cartridges will never be fired except in the direst emergency, and the intent is not to inflict a quick and humane death upon a game animal, but to disable a human being bent upon murder, rape, or assault, whether the shooter is an officer of the law or an honest citizen defending his home and family.

In the autoloaders, the same problems arise in making certain that each round reaches the chamber smoothly that were mentioned in the re-

Recovery of fired bullets from game or test media provides essential data for bullet selection. At left, the 148-grain hollow-based wadcutter loaded backwards shattered upon impact, maximizing shock but minimizing penetration; the 110-grain hollowpoint expanded fully but lost little weight, penetrating more deeply; and the 110-grain soft point expanded well but punched more deeply into the target's vitals. All were fired at maximum velocities from a 4⅝-inch-barreled revolver.

marks on autoloading target pistols, except that we can accept a bit of bullet-nose deformation at ranges which average about 5 to 7 yards. In general, the same solutions apply as well. The important thing is that the load be tested in the gun in which it will be fired until no doubt whatever lingers about its reliability in feeding, extraction, and ejection. This will involve firing not less than fifty rounds of the load from the clip. Even a single jam or failure to feed is one too many, and the cause must be iden-

The Thompson-Center "Contender" single-shot pistol has interchangeable barrels available in a wide variety of chamberings and is in a class by itself for power and flat trajectory for hunting.

tified and a cure found. In some cases, the cure will be found in alterations of the pistol itself—a new magazine, polishing the feed ramp, or a
new extractor spring. Perhaps the most common such alteration is a set of
adjustable sights for a handgun which has fixed sights which do not put
the most effective defense load on the point of aim.

About the only other category of handguns which hasn't been dealt
with here is that of the "hand-rifles," the single-shot varminters such as
the Remington XP-100 or the Thompson-Center Contender. Actually,
the latter is chambered in a number of big-game cartridges as well as varmint numbers. These are specialized handguns, usually equipped with
telescopic sights, and they have barrels which incorporate the chamber as
do rifle barrels, rather than a gap between chamber and barrel in the
fashion of revolvers. For all practical purposes, they *are* rifles without a
buttstock, and handloading ammunition for them is performed in precisely the same manner as for rifles.

Whatever their purposes, belt guns call for a bit of extra care, both
in loading for them and in shooting them. Perhaps the greatest value in
reloading pistol ammunition is that it allows a shooter a greater degree of
familiarity with his guns than anyone who limits himself to factory-made
cartridges, and in handguns, above all, familiarity is the secret to success.

22

Tools for
Metallic Cartridges

Rifle and handgun cartridges can be reloaded, in a pinch, with a few simple tools scrounged or homemade from bits of scrap metal. I suspect that I could find all the necessary items to assemble reasonably functional cartridges in the rear end of my station wagon at this moment. Decapping can be performed with an ice pick or long, slender nail. Case necks can be squeezed down by forcing them into any sort of orifice of a diameter not too much smaller than the bullets which are to be seated in them, even a hole drilled through a piece of hardwood. Primers can be started in their pockets with the fingers and seated by cautiously tapping the case against a piece of hardwood. Powder can be measured—in loads well below maximum—in any sort of makeshift dipper, and bullets can be started and seated by hand. The result may not be as sophisticated or as pretty as ammo loaded in good dies, but it will function and fire safely and might, in a raw survival situation, save your life.

That's doing it the hard way, however, especially with the variety and quality of relatively inexpensive tools on today's market for home-processing metallic ammunition.

The basic tool is a press, which can be visualized as nothing more than a simple machine to multiply the strength of a man's fingers and to direct that force conveniently. The simplest such tools are the various

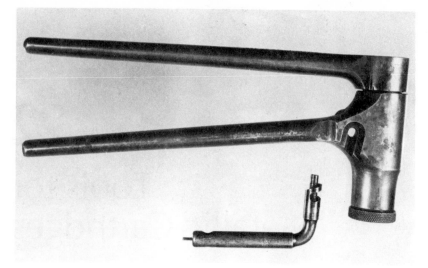

This is a reloading tool sold by Winchester in the 1880s that still functions perfectly. The L-shaped separate piece is for de- and re-capping. Such tools are valuable collectors' items today.

portable, or table-top, models which do not require permanent mounting. The Lee Loaders, the ancient Lyman 310 "tong tool," and the English "Pak-Tool" are examples. These can be used anywhere and stored in a container no bulkier than a cigar box. Several years ago, when my home was severely damaged by fire, I lived in a rented apartment for several months while the house was being rebuilt. I had no place to set up a regular reloading bench in my temporary quarters, and much of my equipment was in storage to which I had no access. I did have most of my components available, and I had an English Pak-Tool, plus a powder scale and a set of Lee's graduated powder dippers. With that equipment, I merrily reloaded handgun, varmint rifle, plinking, and even big-game rifle ammo for more than three months. True, I kept loads well below maximum, but they were by no means pip-squeak loadings, and they delivered accuracy which was every bit as good as I knew my guns to be capable of. With them, I punched a lot of paper and a few jackrabbits, coyotes, bobcats, crows, and javelinas during those months and felt in no way handicapped, at least for that off-season shooting.

The only drawbacks to such tools are that production of loaded rounds is somewhat slower with them than with a good bench-mounted press, and that they cannot full-length resize large rifle cases. The preci-

Everything necessary to assemble good, safe, highly-accurate handloads without a permanent loading-bench setup is shown in this picture. The tool set is a Lee Benchrest set, and the powder dipper is also by Lee. A powder scale, funnel, and chamfering-deburring tool, plus the mallet, complete the necessary equipment for kitchen-table handloads.

Non-bench-mounted reloading tools like this English "Pak-Tool" can put together fine ammunition at minimum cost anywhere. Production rates are low but adequate for most rifle reloading, and the hand tools cannot full-length re-size most bottlenecked cases.

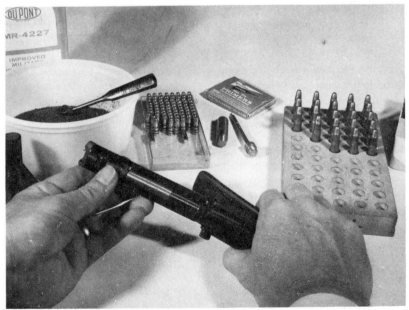

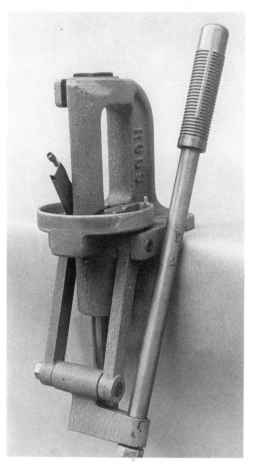

The popular RCBS Rockchucker press is an example of the "O" or "D" configuration, offering exceptional rigidity for its weight for such heavy-duty jobs as bullet swaging and radical case reforming.

sion of which such tools are capable may be illustrated by the fact that those far-gone accuracy nuts, the benchrest shooters, routinely load their ammunition with somewhat more carefully made versions of them. They are also somewhat less expensive, on the average, than bench-mounted presses and dies, and represent a way for a beginner to get into reloading without an elaborate bench or a large initial investment.

Despite the virtues of the portable tools, however, virtually all serious reloading hobbyists sooner or later acquire a bench-type unit, and these are available in quite a variety of styles and price ranges. The simplest is the so-called "C" tool which forms the basic element of almost

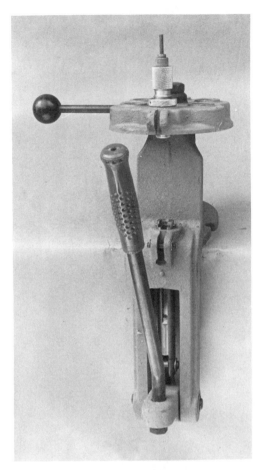

This massive turret tool from Redding is typical of metallic presses of its kind.

every reloading-equipment manufacturer's line. This is essentially an open-faced frame with the die held in place at the top in alignment with a vertically moving ram which carries the shell-holder and is driven via a more or less elaborate mechanical linkage by a hand-operated lever. There is a swinging primer-seating arm which enters a slot in the face of the ram and delivers a primer through a hole in the center of the shell-holder. About the only possible elaborations of the C-press are a spent-primer catcher and some sort of automatic primer feed. Some can be made to operate with either an upstroke or a downstroke, depending upon the operator's preference and the type of mounting.

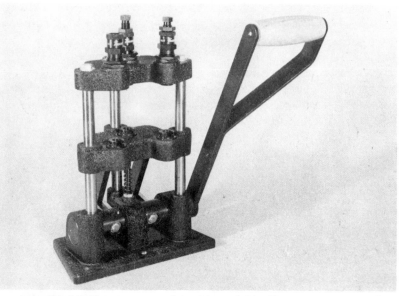

A modified "H" type press such as this model by Texan can accommodate three different dies and shellholders at once, speeding up the loading process, especially of handgun ammunition.

A few of the separate priming tools offered: from left, the Bonanza, Lee, and two different RCBS models.

A well-made C-press will serve about 98 percent of anyone's hand-loading purposes, and will do it for a lifetime. Different models may vary somewhat in their mechanical advantage, but all have enough power for normal reloading jobs. The *potential* liability in this type of press is that it's conceivable that it could spring slightly under very heavy pressure (only applied in bullet-swaging or extreme case-reforming jobs) and thus lose perfect alignment between die and ram. Most C-tools are heavily built and well designed, and springing is definitely not a problem in normal operations. This is the type of press most reloaders start with, and probably the majority never see any reason to change.

If they do change, it will most likely be to one of the so-called "O"-type presses, which are much like C-presses except that the frame is cast so that there is a structural element placed to resist that potential springing mentioned above. The open face of the O is usually to the sides or slightly angled, but is to the front in a few models. Leverage and other features, within a given manufacturer's line, are usually the same as on the C-press. The disadvantage of the O-frame (some makers call it a D-frame) is that it interferes to some extent with manual access to the shell-holder, especially for left-handed persons.

The next step in this alphabetical galaxy of tools is the "H"-style press, which really differs little from a sideways "O" except that the frame is not in one piece. Instead, the die-holder portion is supported at the top of a pair of sturdy posts which serve as guides of the shell-holder portion, which slides up and down. Some H-presses have as many as three die positions, which speeds up production, especially of handgun ammo.

Then we have the turret presses, which have from four to six die positions in a rotating turret. These are particularly handy for a reloader who loads only one or two calibers, in that he can leave all his dies in place and properly adjusted at all times. He may also mount a powder measure in one of the positions in the turret for accelerated production. Only the most massive of the turret presses are entirely free of the springing problem, however, and they tend to be quite expensive.

On these basic designs appear several unclassifiable variations. Pacific offers a big C-press with three die positions and three rams. Bonanza's famous "Co-Ax" is unlike anything else on the market, although reminiscent, at a glance, of a modified H-press. Belding and Mull even sells a press which operates horizontally instead of vertically. The Star progressive tools are the ultimate in production capacity, producing a loaded round with every handle stroke and requiring the operator to do nothing more than feed empty cases to the machine, operate the handle, and remove loaded rounds.

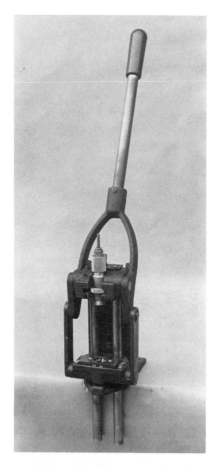

The unique Bonanza Co-Ax press features snap-in, snap-out die installation and a self-acting, nearly universal shellholder, plus sensitive overhead priming.

Generally, quality in the press (ram-die alignment, no skimping on material in the frame, finish, and linkage power) is more important to serious reloading than fancy features, and I prefer to pay my money for the former. If extra-heavy-duty service is required, such as swaging jacketed bullets or unusually severe case reforming, by all means select an O-press or H-press; it will be cheaper in the long run.

Powder scales and measures, case trimmers, priming tools, and various gauges have all been discussed elsewhere in this text. There are, however, a few other small or specialized tools and necessaries which will facilitate any reloader's work, regardless of his choice of presses.

One of these is the powder funnel, customarily a short-spouted plastic funnel with an inside diameter in the spout which tapers so that

The RCBS (foreground) and Forster case trimmers are among the better-known tools of this type.

almost any case can be loaded through the funnel from .22 caliber through at least .45 caliber. Special .17 caliber funnels are on the market, but cases larger than .45, such as the black-powder buffalo cartridges and some British big-game numbers, will require a bit of improvisation. A firm named MTM Moulded Products offers a powder funnel with a detachable 4-inch drop tube which is invaluable for packing heavy charges into cases in which the best loads are often compressed by seating the bullet. Occasionally a recommended powder charge will actually overflow

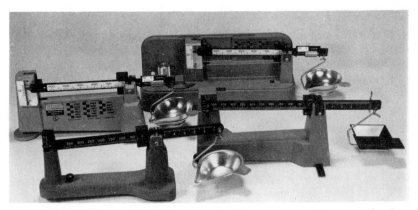

Powder scales come in all degrees of refinement, convenience, and price, but all do the same job well. From front to rear, these are by Redding, Bonanza, RCBS, and Ohaus.

the case; when this happens, recheck your loading data and, if you find it correct, reach for the long-spouted funnel. It's amazing how much more powder such a long drop tube can deposit in the same case volume.

Sooner or later, every reloader will find himself faced with the problem of *un*loading ammunition, either to salvage the components or because a loading has proved too hot in his gun. There are two kinds of bullet pullers common today. One is mounted in the loading press and grips the bullet firmly while the shell-holder pulls the case away from it. The other resembles a hollow-headed hammer with a device to hold the case head. When the puller is banged against a hard surface (just as though the operator were driving a nail with it); inertia pulls the bullet. Of the two types of bullet pullers, the press-mounted is probably faster and requires less effort, but the inertia type delivers all components undamaged and ready for reuse. The latter is also adaptable to almost any cartridge (*don't* try it with rimfires!), while the press-mounted pullers require a different collet for each caliber. Take your pick; they both work. One tip: if your inertia puller seems stubborn on old handloads, factory loads, or surplus military stuff, set up your bullet-seating die in that caliber and adjust the seating stem to seat the bullets just 1/16th inch or so deeper. This will break whatever seal may have developed and make pulling the bullets much easier.

Measuring equipment has been mentioned from time to time, but it really cannot be overemphasized. The two basic tools are a machinist's micrometer for ultra-precise measurements on bullets or case-head diameters to the fourth decimal place, and a precision caliper, either vernier or dial-reading, of at least 4-inch capacity. These normally cannot be read closer than about half a thousandth of an inch, but that's sufficient for many handloading jobs. The greater capacity of the caliper also makes it handy for use as a snap-gauge in sorting cases by length and similar tasks. Any serious reloader of metallic cartridges should have these two tools, at least, on his bench.

An obvious essential is the loading block, a wooden or plastic tray with holes in which cases will stand steadily. The only comment called for is that blocks with different-size holes are necessary for standard, small rifle, and magnum cases. The .45-70 and similar cases require a size larger than the belted magnums, and usually have to be homemade by the reloader. It's well to have two of each size, one in which primed cases stand neck-down until they are picked up for charging, and another into which to place them after powder has been added. Put one block on each side of the powder measure or scale, and you have a built-in procedure for guarding against double charges or no charge rounds.

A loading block is an essential accessory around the loading bench. You can make your own, or buy any of several plastic or wooden commercial versions.

An inertia bullet-puller that will handle almost all cartridges and calibers is a handy accessory; sooner or later, every reloader will need one.

Primers are dumped into this "flipper" tray, which is then shaken gently sideways. Every primer will turn anvil up. If the primers are desired anvil down, the cover is put on and the tray inverted.

Another handy and inexpensive item is the primer flipper, a shallow plastic tray with concentric ridges molded into the bottom. Primers (rifle or pistol only; softshell primers will not work) are dumped into the tray which is shaken gently from side to side. All the primers will be turned anvil-down, which facilitates loading them into a primer-feed tube. If the system requires that they be anvil-up, the lid is put on the tray and the flipper inverted. Even if an automatic primer feed is not featured on your loading equipment, a flipper is useful in reducing the necessary handling of the caps, which, in turn, reduces the chance of primer contamination by oil or grease on the fingers. Offered by RCBS, Fitz, Pacific, Bonanza, Bair, and Herter's, primer turners are all essentially identical.

Bonanza sells another gadget I've been using for a long time, called a case graphiter. It's a small plastic tray with three different-size bristle brushes mounted in it pointing upward. Powdered graphite is placed in the tray and a case neck pushed down over the brush of appropriate caliber and withdrawn just before sizing. The graphiter deposits a bit of graphite both inside and outside the neck, for quieter, easier sizing and less stretching of the case upon withdrawal of the expander button from the neck. This gimmick costs less than $4 as of this writing, and is well worth the investment. Only dry lubes should be used inside a case neck, since liquid or gel-type lubricants catch powder grains when the case is charged and may even inhibit ignition and burning of the powder.

This Bonanza case-neck graphiter lubes the insides of rifle case necks for easier withdrawal of the expander button.

As time goes by, every reloader accumulates a collection of dozens of other gimmicks and gadgets, according to his own experience and needs. There are far too many available to be discussed here, but you can bet that if there's any conceivable use for a certain gilhickey on the loading bench, somebody makes and sells it. Now and then one comes to my attention for which I can't figure out any conceivable use, for that matter. Some of these do exactly what their manufacturers claim they will, but I can't imagine why anyone would want to do it. But it may be just what you're looking for. If you have a problem, ask around; chances are there's something on the market which will solve it, no matter how abstruse or exotic the need.

23

Organizing the Loading Bench

A chapter with such a title is mandatory in every reloading book, and usually winds up reflecting the author's particular preferences and habits, being less applicable to another reloader's needs or to the space he has available. I promise to try to avoid inflicting my own idiosyncrasies upon the reader herein, and to confine myself to the great Universal Truths of organizing a bench.

The first of these is that systems and routines are vital to satisfaction and safety in reloading. One example was mentioned in the previous chapter, in the discussion of loading blocks. Imagine yourself with a tray full of primed brass, ready for powder charges. If the brass is sitting neck-up in the block, and each case is picked up, charged, and returned to the same block, there's an obvious danger that one or more cases will receive a double charge of powder, or that some will receive no charge at all. A friend of mine once hurriedly loaded twenty rounds on the night before deer season opened, and somehow managed to skip a row of five cases in the charging step. He also neglected the visual inspection of charged cases, and wound up with one-quarter of his hunting loads duds. Fortunately, this oversight did not cost him a big buck that season, and the powderless cartridges were not discovered until he began to shoot up that ammunition on the range after the season, but marks on the cases made it clear that those five rounds had been in and out of the rifle's magazine and chamber several times.

This sort of thing couldn't have happened if he'd used the two-block charging system. In this procedure, the primed cases would have been standing neck-down in one block on the left of the powder measure. Thus, none of them could have had powder in it by any imaginable accident when it was picked up, positioned under the measure's drop-tube, and charged. A second block, on the right of the powder measure, would then receive the charged rounds. This sort of routine becomes a fixed habit, and the reloader comes to consider any case which is neck-up in a loading block as charged, which is not a bad thought pattern to form. The formation of habits at the loading bench is inevitable, so one might as well strive to form those which contribute to efficiency and safety.

Another example is the habit of having no more than one can of powder on the bench top at any time, that one being the can from which the powder in the measure came. Then there can be no chance of emptying the measure into the wrong can. If a faster-burning propellant is placed unknowingly in a can with a label indicating a much slower powder, serious consequences can arise if the handloader happens not to notice the difference in appearance, if any, when next he loads his measure from that can. If he dumps full charges of what he assumes is IMR 3031 but is really IMR 4198 into his large rifle cases and fires them, he's staring disaster in the eye at close range!

Many routines are established not so much to avoid accidents as to speed up loading. In setting up a shotshell press, for example, the fellow who devotes a little deep thought and study to the placement of his various components—primers, empty hulls, and wads—so as to reduce the number of hand motions required in processing a round of ammunition will very easily be able to increase his output by about one 25-round box per hour with most common loaders.

And he, like the metallic reloader, makes certain that only the correct components for the load being assembled are within reach, to preclude absentmindedly stuffing the wrong goodies into the case.

Every handloader will have to devise his own procedures and routines to fit his needs and the available space. The important thing is that you be conscious of the value of such routines, habits, and systems, and work out those which suit you. Some experimenting with the placement of major pieces of equipment on your bench is well worthwhile before permanently bolting down the tools. This can usually be done by using C-clamps to hold things in place while ammo is actually being loaded, making minor adjustments as you go to suit your right- or left-

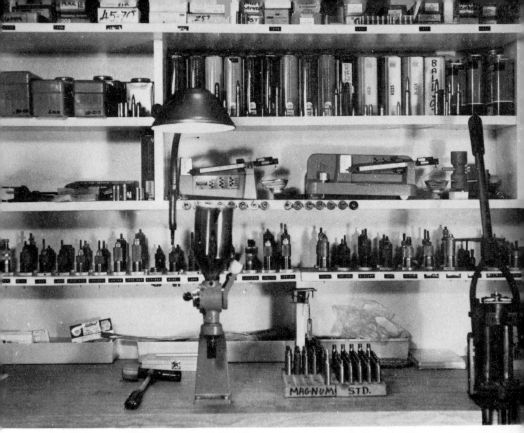

A portion of the author's present loading bench is pictured here, showing storage shelves proportioned to the components for which they'll be used, the elevated position of the two scales, and the adjustable lamp. Note, too, the shell holders hung on nails in the front of the shelf on which the scales sit, the magnet holding small tools just above the loading blocks, and the manner in which the shelves are drilled for die storage.

handedness, your reach, and your manner of doing things. In fact, I never bolt or screw anything down at all, except for my press and powder measure. Everything else is mounted on ¾-inch plywood bases and affixed temporarily with said C-clamps. This includes case trimmers, bench-mounted separate priming tools, case gauges, and even shotshell-loading tools. If one is blessed with unlimited bench space (especially "frontage"), he can save a little time by permanently mounting all these items so that they don't interfere with each other, but not many of us are that fortunate.

The placement of powder scales is important; ideally, they should be mounted at eye level, so that you don't have to bend over like a heron stalking a frog to read the swinging pointer without parallax. I built a special shelf for two scales above my bench, and never move them.

Another special shelf is a die rack, drilled with ⅞-inch holes to accept reloading dies. A 6-inch-wide board, ¾-inch thick, will take three such

This steel die rack, made by RCBS, is handy for organizing dies and shell-holders.

holes (for three-die pistol sets and such) on 2-inch centers. It's probably better to keep dies in the boxes in which they're packed by the maker, but when your collection of calibers exceeds about four, the process of rummaging up the right box from a drawer becomes laborious, and at twenty is intolerable. A cloth can be draped over the die shelf when the bench is not in use to keep dust from the precious dies, and they should get an occasional light spray of corrosion-inhibiting lubricant.

A really good light is absolutely essential at the loading bench. In addition to whatever area lighting is available, by all means invest in a gooseneck or draftsman-type fixture which permits some flexibility. With it, you can position the bulb properly for inspecting the level of powder in charged cases, for example, and read delicate verniers without going blind. Inspecting brass before loading demands good light, as does inspecting cast bullets. All in all, I probably should have put the light at the first of this chapter; it's that important.

One of the world's handiest gadgets on a loading bench is a small permanent magnet screwed to the front of a shelf or to the wall. I use one

A couple of magnets screwed to the front of loading-bench shelves are super handy for keeping such things as allen wrenches and small screwdrivers available.

of these to keep track of the assortment of small tools, especially the various Allen wrenches every reloader uses constantly, plus small screwdrivers, flash-hole gauges, and primer-pocket tools. A row of such magnets would be a very neat way of keeping the various shell-holders sorted and easily available, but I use a simple row of small finishing nails driven into the front of a shelf. The same system serves for powder and shot bushings for my shotshell loaders; these bushings are seldom made of ferrous metal, and the magnet idea won't work for them.

One solution to the problem of limited (or no) bench space has just appeared on the market. It's called a Porta-Post and is just that, a metal post with a mounting plate by which a reloading press can be affixed to its top. The whole rig can be moved around with relatively little danger of double hernia, stored in a closet, and set up instantly for use. The height of the mounted press is correct for comfortable use while seated in an ordinary chair, and the Porta-Post is surprisingly stable in service. Even with a fairly generous bench surface, I keep a press set up on my Porta-Post at all times for certain special jobs for which I don't want to tie up my regular bench-mounted tool.

The Republic "Porta-Post" is one solution to the no-space-for-a-loading-press problem.

An ordinary small-parts cabinet built into the loading bench complex greatly facilitates organization of bullets, primers, and small tools.

Components storage on, under, or around the loading bench should be given a bit of thought from the point of view of safety. Primers of various sorts and sizes are probably best organized in one of the multi-drawered small-parts cabinets whose plastic drawers will hold about six boxes of rifle or pistol primers. If you buy primers by the thousand, store the rest elsewhere. Keep only those types of powder which you use regularly within reach of the bench, and store other types and quantities in your powder magazine. Never keep more powder in an open container, including your powder measure, than you have immediate use for, and never store primers and powder in close proximity to each other. Warnings about storage of primers *only* in the factory packaging bear repeating.

Finally, keep a fire extinguisher within easy reach at the loading bench and close to every other area where powder or primers are kept.

24

Reloading
Record-Keeping

I am not a guy who enjoys keeping records. I have trouble keeping my checkbook balanced, and am the despair of the IRS when it's audit time. But I can show you, in five minutes or less, the full dope on *every* handload, without any exceptions, I've ever put together. Record-keeping is a pain in the posterior, but it's vital to handloading progress and safety. If you neglect it, the day will come when you will regret it, and you can write that down and say I said it!

For any single cartridge, there are literally thousands of different possible combinations of powder, charge weight, and bullet, not to mention primers, brass, and other variables. Even if you stick with only one bullet weight, brand, and style, there are hundreds of possibilities. No human being can keep in mind forever every formula ever tested in a given cartridge, much less group sizes, velocities, trajectory data, recoil sensation, pressure symptoms, and all the other observations made while firing each combination. If a reloader loads for four or five cartridges, or twenty, he'll have to have the mental storage banks of a computer to get by without record-keeping.

Good records are more than a convenience or merely a means to avoid duplication of past efforts; they can facilitate the development of a new load by presenting data on past experiments in an orderly fashion which suggests logical avenues for further improvement. They can save a great deal of work by reminding the reloader that a certain rifle seems to prefer one powder over another, or that a given bullet in that rifle needs a certain minimum velocity to stabilize properly, or a specific lot of brass has been fire-formed in one particular rifle.

Most custom bullet manufacturers pack gummed labels with their bullets which can be attached to an ammo box and which have blank spaces for filling in the pertinent data. These are handy for identifying the load in the box, but they are not intended to serve as adequate reloading records. Some sort of permanent records system is still required, and it should be complete, easily stored, and capable of preserving your data in readily retrievable form.

At the very minimum, this system should include *all* of the following for *each* loading:

date loaded	primer brand
number of rounds	primer size and type
charge weight	case brand
powder designation	times fired (cases)
bullet brand	range
bullet weight	group sizes
bullet style	velocity
notes on pressure	
signs, purpose of	
load, etc.	

Additional data on the load which are desirable if not absolutely necessary include powder lot number, primer lot number, an identifying number or code for each different loading, and sundry other notes and observations from firing tests, such as recoil, blast, consistency, case-head expansion measurements, temperature and weather conditions during firing, and anything else which will help in future load development.

Quite a few manufacturers have attempted to publish handloaders' record books, most of them set up with one or perhaps two loads per page. This demands an enormous amount of writing, especially in, for example, a pressure series in which nothing changes from load to load except the powder charge weight. Being lazy, years ago I developed a reloading records system of my own which spared me vast amounts of repetitive scribbling. This system arranged all the data for each load in vertical columns, so that I could use ditto marks for those elements which did not change. I have used this system for almost twenty years now, and it has proved to have quite a few unforeseen advantages.

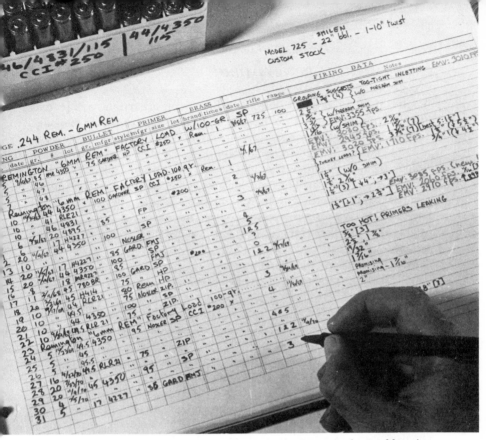

Illustrated here is a typical page from the author's personal record-keeping system, described in detail in the text. Sheets are mimeographed on legal-size paper and stored in a three-ring binder. Note that more than three years' work with this cartridge are reflected on this one page, and note also the ease with which data on any component can be extracted, while ditto marks eliminate repetitive writing.

It keeps data in a very compact form, so that many years' experience with dozens of different cartridges is easily stored in a single loose-leaf binder. Furthermore, the data is presented so that it's easy to retrieve, merely by running a finger down a column. For example, if I'm curious as to whether I ever tried IMR 3031 powder in the .308 WCF case, I can run down the "powder" column on my home-designed, mimeographed form over three or four pages and extract every 3031 load ever fired in that cartridge.

I may very well not be the originator of the ditto-data idea (there's very little new under the sun in any aspect of handloading), but I was certainly the first writer to present the idea in various magazines and annuals catering to shooters. Recently, not one but two firms have introduced handloading record books patterned directly on my system, accidentally or otherwise. Although I am in no way connected with these companies and receive no royalties or other compensation (my form was never copyrighted and was offered freely in my articles), I shall refrain from mentioning the names of these products here. Your reloading dealer doubtless can show them to you. They may or may not be an improvement on my original system, according to the varying needs of different individuals. In any case, my own form is reproduced here and anyone is free to adopt or modify it as he chooses for his own use. I can state that it has stood the test of my own experience and thousands of different loads for scores of cartridges and I can think of no way to improve it for my own needs.

From left to right, under the heading *LOADING*, you will find columns headed #, *No.*, and *Date*. The first is my numerical code for the particular loading, the *No.* refers to the number of rounds of that combination assembled, and *Date* is the date I put them together. Totaling the numbers under the *No.* heading gives the total number of rounds fired in that rifle (or caliber, at least), and may eventually give an indication of barrel life, among other things.

Under *POWDER*, we have columns headed *Gr.* (charge weight in grains); #, which refers to powder designation (usually a number); and *Lot*. Lot numbers are stamped on powder canisters, and, since certain powders are known to change characteristics from lot to lot, may be a

Commercial handloaders' record-keeping system similar to author's is available in loose-leaf binder from MTM.

The handloader can save himself time by devising a notation system for recording settings on his powder measure for oft-used loads. However, he must still check charge weights on a powder scale when returning to any specific setting.

valuable bit of data for safety purposes or to unravel the causes of mysterious pressure signs.

The *BULLET* heading is self-explanatory, including columns for *Gr.* (weight), *Mfgr.* (maker), and *Style*. The last column may be filled with such notes as *RN* (roundnose), *HP* (hollow-point), *FMJ* (full metal jacket), and *SPZ* (spitzer).

Under *PRIMER* will be found three columns which seem to me to be self-explanatory, *Mfgr.* (brand), *Size*, and *Lot*. Most manufacturers give their large rifle magnum primers a different size designation from that of their large rifle standard caps, and this number goes into the *Size* column. Primer lots are stamped on the boxes.

Surely neither *Brand* nor *Times* heading under *BRASS* requires much explanation, except that *Times* refers to the number of times these cases have been fired.

The final major heading, *FIRING DATA*, includes columns for the date fired, the particular rifle in which the tests were conducted, the distance at which the firing occurred, and a space for notes. The *Notes* column always includes group sizes (and number of shots per group in brackets) and velocity (if chronographed). In browsing back through my data book, I find many other notes to myself in this column, concerning observations of seating depths, warnings that certain loads are "TOO

HOT!" or that the load was worked up for African game and slew this or that animal. Sometimes I refer myself to "Load #103" of the same cartridge, for a comparison of velocity or some other aspect which interests me about it.

The data book always goes to the rifle range with me, and I enter appropriate data while it's fresh in my mind. I also maintain a 5 × 8-inch loose-leaf notebook which is a sort of journal of shooting activities and a catch-all notebook for any dope for which there's no room in the data forms. In this book I keep all manner of oddball observations, outline future loading programs, maintain complete chronograph data (only corrected muzzle velocities go into the data book forms), record powder-measure settings for pet loads, and jot down theories and speculations on how to improve performances in various guns.

In this book, by the way, are kept all shotshell reloading data (all the above applies to metallic cartridges only), including all components of each shotshell load plus patterning analyses, pressure and velocity where known, and general performance notes.

These two books represent the distilled experience gained from almost a quarter-century of handloading ammunition, and there is a rather peculiar effect which develops through such note-taking. Each bit of information recorded comes to amplify and illuminate all the other bits, so that the body of data accumulated really does exceed the sum of its parts. Over the years, the contents of these binders have proved to be by far the most valuable source of reloading information I have, far more useful in my guns and for my purposes than any amount of commercially published handloading dope. With faithful and meticulous record-keeping, so will yours. The real worth of my collection of data was brought home painfully to me when my home burned. I was away from the city at the time, and had several hours' drive to get home after the news of the fire reached me. All the way home, through the small hours of the morning, I found myself wondering fearfully if my reloading records had been destroyed. I was concerned, of course, about all the contents of the house, but those irreplaceable records worried me most. When I discovered that they were safe, if smoke-smudged, I speedily had every page of both my data book and my journal photocopied and tucked the copies away in a safe place. It may be argued that I make my living writing about such matters, and that my accumulation of data was more valuable to me than a hobbyist's, and that may be true from a dollars-and-cents viewpoint. Still, every reloader's records are priceless for his own purposes, and the idea of photocopying them for safe storage, perhaps annually, is a very sound one.

25

Loading for the Shotgun

According to sales figures on all kinds of small-arms primers, about 60 percent of all cartridges reloaded in America are shotshells, and the total amounts to more than 600 million rounds annually. The great majority of these are target loads, to be fired at clay pigeons over skeet and trap ranges. A serious competitor at either of these games has no choice but to handload his practice ammunition, unless he happens to have about a six-figure income, simply because he shoots so much. He may average 50 to 100 rounds per day, perhaps three or more days each week, whereas four or five five-shot groups is a fair day's shooting for the average rifleman-reloader.

Except for those who go after mourning doves and such pests as crows, most hunters hardly fire enough shells in the field to justify a loading setup, unless they have need for some special kind of load which isn't available on the commercial market, or unless they just happen to enjoy experimenting, refining, and perfecting shotshell loadings in the same way that riflemen do. Therefore, many gunners reload all practice target ammo, and purchase factory cartridges for hunting.

If economy is the major motivation for handloading shotshells, performance should not be slighted, and it need not be, these days. When I began reloading shotgun ammunition, it was looked upon in most quarters as a sort of occult art. In those days, plastic cases were unheard-of, folded crimps were brand-new, and one-piece wad columns may have been a gleam in somebody's eye but were certainly not available over the counter. We were lucky to get three or four loadings out of a single waxed-paper hull, and we laboriously built up wad columns of nitro cards and filler wads made of fiber, felt, or cork. Plastic shot wrappers were beginning to look like a good idea, and the most revolutionary development in sight was the cupped plastic overpowder wad.

All that has changed in the last twenty years; indeed, shotshell loading has been the fastest-moving of all reloading areas. Tooling, components, and techniques have all seen radical improvements. In the old days, we were reasonably well satisfied if our handloads went BANG and broke an occasional clay bird or peppered a hapless tin can. Today, it's possible to load shotshells which are the full equal of the best factory loads in every respect.

I did say "possible," not "easy." Whereas a rifleman or pistolero routinely expects to improve on factory performance, at least in his own guns, with handloads, the shotgunner does well to *match* commercial ammunition and very rarely betters it. A good deal is written in the sporting press about super shotshell handloads, and such results can be achieved through careful experimenting with an individual gun, but the truth is that the same amount of experimenting with factory loads of various brands and types will usually deliver about equally good results.

Why, then, bother with loading shotshells, except for the cost savings? Well, lowered shooting costs constitute a pretty good reason when we're talking about savings of at least $30 to $40 per case of ammo. Then, too, there are many special-purpose loadings which the factories cannot market economically but which an individual gunner may have a use for. "Brush" or "spreader" loads which can throw improved-cylinder patterns from a full-choke barrel are still catalogued but rarely seen on dealers' shelves. Furthermore, they are available only in 12-gauge with 1⅛ ounces of No. 8 shot, at only one velocity. If you'd like such choke-opening loadings for decoyed ducks with No. 6 shot, or with a heavier shot charge, you'll have to put them together yourself. Conversely, if your barrel is modified and some of your duck shooting is at long range, handloads can probably come closer to delivering really good long-range patterns than can factory ammunition. Very light loads for maximum savings and minimum recoil are not commercially made but can be handloaded very simply. In short, there are quite a few excellent reasons for reloading shotshells besides economy.

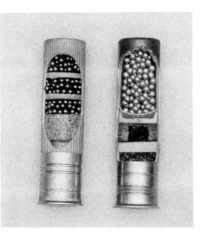

The two extremes of pattern-changing handloads: at left is a spreader load with the shot charge divided by "B"-cards, while at right is a special, long-range load with perforated fill wad, a plastic shot wrapper, and copper-plated shot.

The handloader must shift mental gears when going from metallics to shotshells. Velocity, in and of itself, is not very important in the latter. I suppose that all of us go through a phase of playing with ultra-high velocities in shot charges, but we get over it when we discover that we're killing no more birds, if as many, and soaking up prodigious quantities of recoil in the process. I long ago standardized velocities of all my shotshell loads, in all gauges, between about 1,165 and perhaps 1,215 FPS. The reason is simply that shot pellets, being spheres, have the poorest possible ballistic coefficient and the difference in striking power at game ranges between a pellet which started out at 1,200 FPS and one launched at 1,350 FPS is so small as to be negligible. In the meantime, the high-velocity loading kicks like a mule and rarely delivers patterns as dense and uniform as those from normal-speed ammo.

Another difference between metallic and shotshell cartridges is that the latter must come out at a fixed length, whereas overall length in a rifle cartridge can vary somewhat according to the seating depth selected for the bullet. The contents of a shotshell (powder, wadding, and shot) must stand at exactly the right height in the uncrimped hull, in order to get a good, firm crimp and complete closure. If the volume of one of the components is reduced, that of one of the others must be increased by the same amount. Otherwise, the crimp will be bulged and may open up enough to leak shot, or it will be dished and loose. Either condition is likely to cause abnormally high variations in velocity from shot to shot, since a firm, uniform crimp is perhaps the most important factor in uniform ignition and combustion of shotshell powders. Adjustment of the

The key to satisfactory shotshell stuffing lies in proper matching of all the components in the load, the right wad in the right case, with the correct powder, charge, and primer. All four of these rounds do the same thing, but use three different hull types, three different wads, and three kinds of powder. Follow load formulas to the letter for best results.

total volume of components in a shell using one of the one-piece plastic wad columns is simpler, since most of these incorporate a collapsible cushioning section which can be compressed enough in crimping to achieve the desired results. However it's accomplished, though, the reloader must fix the concept of a good crimp—not too deep, not too high, but just right—firmly in mind; it's one of the major keys to good results in shotshell loading.

The critical concept in scattergun feeding is *pattern*. In a rifle, accuracy, velocity, and trajectory are everything; in a shotgun, they're nothing. Pattern is the whole ballgame. A good pattern is what breaks targets or kills birds. A load which patterns poorly in a given gun barrel is useless, regardless of velocity or energy figures. Each of the components in the load has its effect upon patterns. Cases themselves are least important, but a worn-out case cannot hold a firm crimp and thus contributes to variable shot-to-shot performance. The type of powder used does not, in general, make much difference in patterns, but the pressure it generates and the rate at which it generates it can make quite a difference. Fast-burning powders with short, high time-pressure curves accelerate the shot charge more violently, deforming more pellets and causing flyers. Slower-burning

These special transparent-plastic shotshell hulls are used to suggest the tremendous variety of combinations of components available to the reloader. All six loads use the same powder, the same shotcharge, and deliver approximately similar muzzle velocities, but throw very different types of patterns, even in the same gun, due the different wads, which range from a simple nitro card and fiber fillers to plastic, one-piece units.

propellants get the whole column moving a little less abruptly and tend to preserve the perfect roundness of more of the pellets. Deformed pellets are fatal to both density and uniformity in the pattern.

Height of the components column inside a shotshell before crimping determines the success of the crimp. The left-hand examples show correct height and crimp, while the middle pair illustrate a too-low column and the right-hand pair a too-high column.

The wad column, whether one-piece or built-up, serves several functions. First, it must contain the powder gases behind it. Gas which leaks into the shot charge raises hob with patterns. Second, the wad column must cushion the onslaught of the gases, permitting the shot charge to begin its acceleration down the barrel as gently as possible. Otherwise, the pellets at the rear of the charge will be mashed together, deformed, and perhaps even fused into clumps. Third, most modern wad columns incorporate either a plastic cup which carries the shot safely clear of the muzzle or a plastic wrapper intended to protect the pellets from contact with the barrel walls. Either element reduces the scrubbing effect of such contact and, again, delivers more undeformed shot.

Finally, the shot itself has an effect on patterns. Most shot pellets are alloyed to at least a minor degree, rather than being pure lead, but certain brands and kinds are deliberately made much harder than usual. The harder pellets, of course, resist deformation better than soft ones. Some kinds of pellets are copper- or nickel-plated for the same purpose and, although expensive, do pattern better if all else remains the same.

If this brief discussion suggests that the number-one goal in a shotshell load is to get as many of the individual pellets in a shot charge as possible out of the muzzle in a state of pristine sphericity, it has served its purpose. Round pellets fly true; flat-sided or mashed ones spin away at divergent angles and are lost to the pattern.

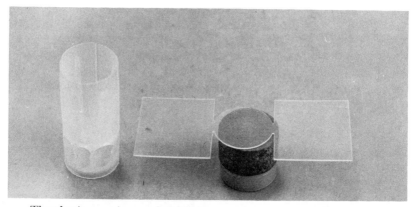

The plastic one-piece wad at left incorporates an over-powder cup, cushioning elements, and a shot cup. At right is a built-up wad column with all the same elements but in separate units. Both give about the same performance; the built-up column is cheaper but slower to assemble.

The second major concept in shotshell patterns which must be firmly grasped is that of the shot charge as a *fluid* mass, rather than a solid. As the charge begins to move under the impulse of powder gases, it is shortened as the rear pellets move before the front ones in the mass. It is then driven out of the case and through the forcing cone in the chamber, being lengthened again as the diameter is reduced. Finally, the shot column must pass through the choke restriction, if any, and again its diameter and length are changed. As it leaves the muzzle, the charge immediately begins to expand in diameter, but it also begins to lengthen as deformed pellets slow down more rapidly than perfect ones. By the time the charge has reached 40 yards it may be as much as 10 feet long and 40 inches or more wide.

Throughout this rather violent journey, the pellets move in relation to each other, and the charge itself, as a whole, does react somewhat as a fluid. Anything which tends to preserve this fluidity (such as cushioning wads or extra-hard pellets) also tends to improve the density and uniformity of resulting patterns. And any element which tends to disrupt the fluidity of the shot charge tends to reduce pattern density, at least, and usually injures pattern uniformity as well. Salt that idea away in the back of your mind and never forget it; it will explain many mysteries and open many doors on the road to shotshell-loading satisfaction.

Patterning your handloads in your shotgun is, obviously, the fundamental process in load-testing. Patterning is a bit of a nuisance and certainly time-consuming if done correctly, but it's the one and only way to know whether you have reached your goal. You can fire one shot at an old cardboard box at some unknown distance and step up and eyeball the little holes . . . and learn exactly nothing whatsoever. Shotshell patterning must be done as systematically as group-shooting with a rifle. There's a great deal more information than one might suspect contained in a stack of fired pattern sheets. It's right there before your eyes, but a little know-how is required to extract it.

First, pattern evaluation should be based on not fewer than five shots with each load, preferably ten. Basic patterning is done at a measured 40 yards, although some special-purpose loads may also be tested at greater or smaller distances. The best and cheapest testing medium is brown wrapping paper, which can be purchased in 4-foot-wide rolls. Sheets of this 4 feet square are suitable for pattern-testing, and can be stapled to a simple wooden frame before a safe backstop. Mark an aiming point at the center of the sheet, step back 40 yards, shoulder the gun, and fire quickly.

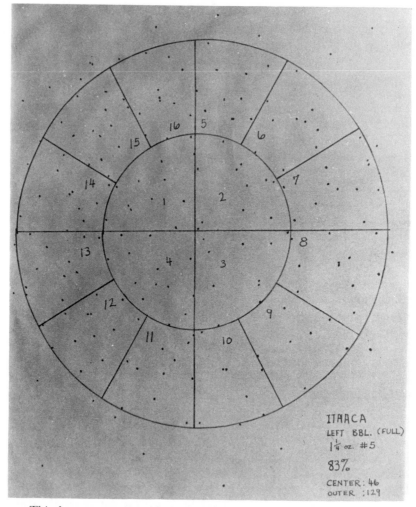

This shotgun pattern, with the 16-field target superimposed upon it, reveals its excellence very clearly. The ratio of pellet hits in the inner circle to those in the outer ring is 1:2.8, showing very little central thickening in pellet distribution. Pellet counts in the individual fields are, in numerical order, 12, 11, 10, 13, 11, 10, 12, 11, 7, 7, 11, 13, 11, 14, and 11; with the exceptions of fields 9 and 10 on the low side and 15 on the high side, the range in number of pellets per field is from 10 to 13, exceptional uniformity, with plenty of coverage for any sort of game on which such a load might be used. This pattern is even, dense, well-balanced, and saturated.

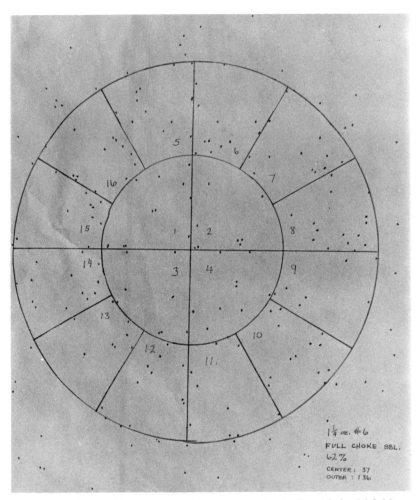

1¼ oz. #6
FULL CHOKE BBL.
62%
CENTER: 37
OUTER: 136

At first glance, this pattern might not appear too bad, until the 16-field target is superimposed; then it is shown to be a very poor pattern indeed. In the first place, although fired from a nominal full-choke barrel, it is a weak modified pattern (there were originally 280 pellets in the charge, but only 173, or 62 percent, struck inside the 30-inch circle). The 1:3.6 ratio of pellets in the center to those in the outer ring shows that the pattern is already beyond its optimum working range, even at 40 yards. Pellet counts in the individual fields range from a low of 7 to a high of 15, revealing very poor distribution, most of the fields have one or more gaping holes through which even a biggish game bird could fly unscathed. A hunter firing this handload would wonder what was wrong with his gun-pointing, when the trouble was actually with his ammunition. The 16-field pattern tells the story.

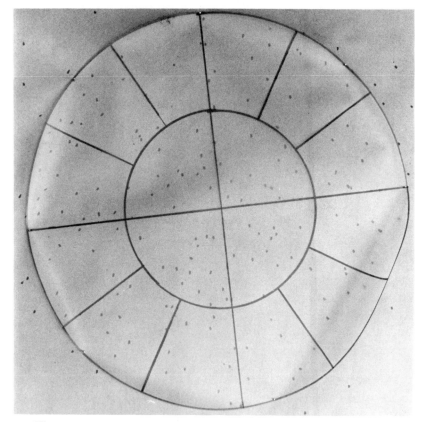

The most convenient way to use the Wannsee 16-field target is to draw it on translucent acetate. When laid over a piece of patterning paper, the pellet holes may be seen and counted through the plastic, saving hours of painstaking drawing of circles and lines on the patterns themselves.

The usual instructions at this point urge you to draw a circle, 30 inches in diameter, which encloses the greatest possible number of pellet holes. The relationship of the center of this circle to the aiming point provides information as to whether your guns shoot where they look, something that's worth knowing. The number of pellet holes inside the circle, as a proportion of the number originally launched, gives a good idea as to whether your barrel actually delivers the degree of choke that's marked on the barrel, with that load and particularly with that shot size. The accompanying tables of pellets per load and choke percentages will facilitate that determination. About the only other bit of information available from your marked-off circles is an eyeball evaluation of any gross patchiness or gaping holes in the pattern.

There is much more to be learned from those riddled sheets of paper, however, knowledge which the serious reloader needs, and here's how to derive it.

Acquire a large sheet of clear plastic such as engineers and draftsmen use for overlays on engineering drawings. This can be had slick both sides, matte both sides, or matte one side, and it really doesn't matter which you can get. On this sheet, with a felt-tipped marking pen, draw a 30-inch circle. Using the same center, draw another circle inside the first one, with a 7½-inch radius, or half the diameter of the outside circle. Now quarter the whole figure with a horizontal and a vertical line, like crosshairs in a rifle scope. Finally, divide the outer ring of the pattern into twelve panels with lines at 30-degree intervals. This sheet of plastic can now be laid over a pattern and moved around to catch the greatest number of pellet holes, and no longer do you need to actually scribe circles on the paper itself. Pellet holes are visible through the plastic.

You now have something called a Berlin-Wannsee sixteen-field target, a remarkably useful instrument for wringing information from a bunch of sheets of paper with shot holes in them. Each of the sixteen areas marked off in the target is equal in area to each of the others, and the ratio of the area of the inner circle to that of the outer, doughnut-shaped ring is 1:3. Specifically, the whole pattern encloses about 707 square inches, the inner circle encloses about 176 square inches, the area of the outer doughnut is about 530 square inches, and each of the sixteen fields amounts to about 44 square inches.

The first measurement to be made after determining the total number of hits inside the 30-inch circle is the distribution of those hits between the inner circle and the outer doughnut. If the doughnut has about three times the number of pellets as the inner circle, that pattern can be considered at its most efficient range. If the inner circle has, say, the same number of hits as the outer ring (in only one-third the area, remember), the pattern is markedly denser in the middle, and will probably spread to maximum uniform coverage at a greater distance. This is one of the marks of a good long-range load, but is highly undesirable in a skeet load where the average range will be about 21 yards.

The evenness of the pattern is revealed by how nearly similar the pellet counts are in the sixteen fields. If the patterns show as few as two or three pellets in some fields and perhaps twenty or more in others, consistently, you can only conclude that this particular loading seems not to deliver uniform patterns in this particular gun. Such patterns will usually reveal several large holes through which a dove or clay pigeon might escape. There is no such thing as a perfect shotgun pattern, however, so a ratio of about 2:1 between the densest and sparsest fields can be considered about normal. Anything better than that is probably coincidental.

Finally, the sixteen-field target can show whether the load being tested has sufficient saturation for the game in question. Many years ago, an Englishman named Sir Gerald Burrard gave us a formula by which we can approximate the target area in square inches of various game birds. According to Burrard, 88 percent of the bird's weight in ounces roughly equals the target of head, neck, and body from typical angles, in square inches. This proportion permits us to relate the areas of our sixteen-field target to the game we intend to hunt with a given handload. A mourning dove weighs about 4.5 ounces. By Burrard's formula, this translates to a target area of only 3.96 square inches, which means that there's room inside our 30-inch circle for no fewer than 178 mourning doves! That gives some insight into just how dense and uniform a pattern must be to reliably kill doves.

On the other hand, an average wild turkey gobbler presents about 261 square inches of target, and would fit into the 30-inch circle 2.7 times. However, more than one hit is obviously required to down a turkey, and pellets must be large for the necessary energy to penetrate heavy feathers. Not less than eight pellets, not smaller than No. 2, are needed, which means that a perfectly distributed pattern of only about twenty-two pellets could do the job on a gobbler. This is the saturation concept. Naturally, since perfect distribution cannot be expected, we'd like to see thirty or forty pellets in the load. Since even a 1¼-ounce load of No. 2s contains 112 pellets, this suggests that for our turkey load, we could go up to one of the smaller buckshot sizes, assuming the gun patterned the larger shot equally well.

One more example: A drake mallard weighs about 45 ounces, which equals just under 40 square inches of profile, or approximately the area of one of the sixteen fields in the Berlin-Wannsee target. Tests have proved that such birds require four to five hits from No. 4 shot for dependable kills. Therefore, a saturated duck load must produce that many holes in each of the fields, at a minimum, plus a safety margin to take care of unequal distribution of shot over the whole 30-inch circle, say a total charge of 120 pellets. Even a ⅞-ounce shot charge of No. 4s has about that many individual pellets, and a 1⅞-ounce 12-gauge 3-inch magnum load has more than twice the maximum necessary lead for ducks.

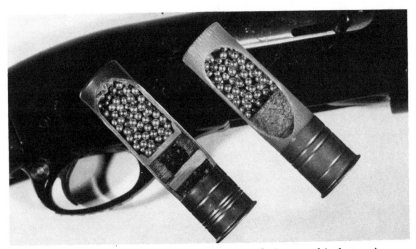

It is frequently possible for a reloader to greatly improve his shotgun's ranging abilities with special handloads. These may be tedious to assemble, but very few are likely to be fired in a season and a full ten yards may be added to the gun's capabilities.

All these things the sixteen-field target can make apparent when it's laid over an innocent-looking sheet of peppered paper. This is the heart of pattern evaluation of handloaded shotshells, and patterning is the backbone of shotgun performance. Based on information from such testing, intelligent decisions can be made about shot sizes, gauges, and chokes. The testing must, of course, be done at the range at which the game in question is most often fired upon.

Every barrel will handle different sizes of shot a little differently. In fact, the choke designation stamped on a shotgun barrel is really only a mechanical measurement of the actual constriction in the choke, and is not a reliable indication of the patterns that barrel will throw. Every barrel has at least two or three different performance levels, depending upon shot size, type, velocity, and other factors in the load. Reloading can, therefore, actually change the choke of a shotgun barrel. In the hands of a handloader, a modified barrel, for example, can usually be made to pattern anywhere from improved cylinder to full choke by varying components.

Considering the cost of additional shotguns, or even extra barrels, that alone isn't a bad reason for reloading shotshells.

26

Shotshell Components

Shotshell loading doesn't lend itself to what might be termed "creative handloading." The name of the metallic reloading game may be trying different combinations until the right one is found, but the handloader of shotgun ammunition is much more limited. The reason is that shotshell powders are very fast-burning, and oddball component combinations can have an unpredictable effect on pressures. This is not to say that substituting components in recommended loadings is necessarily dangerous, or that an occasional good load cannot be developed in such a way. One of the best-performing 12-gauge loads I ever worked up included a Remington case, CCI primer, Alcan powder, and a Winchester wad. Pressure was normal and the PSI spread a very low 700 PSI. Velocity was right on the money at 1,205 FPS, and velocity spread was an unbelievable 8 FPS from the fastest to the slowest shots in a ten-shot string. However, I had access to a modern ballistics laboratory with pressure and velocity measurement equipment when I developed that load. Very few reloaders have such an advantage, and their best insurance against nasty surprises lies in following reliable, published leading recommendations *exactly*, making no substitutions of any kind.

In another test in that same ballistics lab, I once assembled some 20-gauge target ammo precisely according to the Winchester book, using all matched Winchester-Western components. The average velocity of ten shots fell within 3 feet per second of published Winchester factory ammunition velocity. Better than that, no handloader can hope to get!

One reason that sticking to published data in shotshells these days is profitable is that there's so much more reliable, tested data available. A few years ago, a certain daring was fashionable among scattergun loaders simply because only the sketchiest dope was available from manufacturers. Now, with the astonishing growth of shotshell handloading, there's no need to guess. Most publishers of data include loads using components other than those they may manufacture themselves. Winchester-Western, Remington (duPont), Federal, Hercules, Hodgdon, Alcan (Smith & Wesson/Fiocchi), and most other makers of components all offer reams of good data. Find a load that seems to offer the performance you're looking for among these sources and load it, without substitutions. It may not be as exciting as the old way, but it's safer, cheaper, and more satisfactory all the way around.

Shotgun cases have changed with the rest of components, mostly in the direction of all-plastic, compression-formed hulls. Federal still makes paper target cases, and they can sometimes be acquired in large quantities at reasonable prices around target ranges. They load well, but wear out rapidly. Most cases the reloader will encounter, however, are plastic. In once-fired form, they may cost up to 4¢ apiece, but you'll probably lose them before you wear them out in reloading. They have no separate base wads to shoot loose, and they retain a strong "crimp memory." Repeated loading and firing of plastics does weaken them slightly, but the only effect seems to be a minor reduction in velocities. It's not uncommon to get eight or ten reloads out of a compression-formed case, and manufacturers these days emphasize reloadability of their cases in their advertising—which is a far cry from a decade or so ago, when they printed scare-tactic warnings against reloading on the boxes in which factory ammunition was packed.

By far the best bet for a reloader is standardization on one type of shotshell case for which he has a steady source of supply. He can then stock appropriate wads, powders, and primers in large enough quantities to get a price break, and set up his loading equipment more or less permanently for that type of case.

Standardizing primers is also a sage idea, but the powder being loaded is more important to primer selection today than the case brand or type. There are distinct differences in shotshell primers on the market, although none—as of this writing—are styled "magnums" by their makers. My tests show Winchester-Western, Federal, and Alcan caps to be "hotter" than CCI or Remington, for example. Hotter, of course, does not mean better or, for that matter, worse; it merely means that primers shouldn't be substituted in tested loading data in the handbooks. My tests also suggest, but do not prove conclusively, that matching a given manufacturer's primers with his own powders is never a mistake. In any case, follow the recommendations.

Many of the shotshell powders on today's market have been around forever, seemingly, and are still going strong. Hercules Red Dot, Unique, Herco, and Remington's PB are among the classics, not to mention the old Alcan favorites with which most of us started after World War II. Newer powders, however, have offered a wider choice and some advantages. The Olin-made Ball shotshell powder propellants are very dense and permit more latent energy to be packed into a smaller space. They also measure very uniformly through a shotshell tool's charge bar, for more uniform ballistics. Some of the newer propellants are far cleaner-burning as well. Again, follow the recommendations.

Follow the charge-weight recommendations, too. As I said, shotshell powders are very quick-burning, and "an extra pinch for good measure" can get you into trouble. I once developed a 20-gauge hunting load which performed beautifully in laboratory tests, but fell just a few feet per second short of the target velocity. I upped the charge weight just .5 grain— and watched pressures soar into the danger region. It's surprising how an adjustment of as little as .2 grain of powder in a shotshell can smooth out pressure and velocity variations, but such adjustments must be held within the limits of maximum published loads.

I'm a stickler for exact charge weights in shotgun ammunition. When I put a new powder bushing or bar into service, I run quite a few rounds through the loader, checking every charge on my scale. If the charge is consistently light, I'll polish out the cavity with emery cloth on a wooden dowel chucked into an electric drill until it's dropping the nominal weight of powder each and every time. If the new bushing drops too heavy a charge, I'll use plastic tape in the cavity to reduce its capacity. When the bushing delivers precisely the charge I want, plus or minus not more than .2 grain, I mark the bushing and use it for that powder and charge exclusively. It may sound like a lot of trouble over very minor differences, but little things mean a lot in handloading ammunition of any kind.

Incidentally, when taking powder charges for weighing, the loading tool must be operated in exactly the same manner as when ammo is actually being loaded. The bumps and jars to which the equipment is subjected during the loading cycle tend to settle the powder in the bushing in a certain way, and a deviation in the cycle can produce a significantly different charge weight. Late one night, I was assembling a couple of boxes of shotshells for a quail hunt and found myself without a powder bushing which threw the charge I needed. I did have one, however, which dropped a half-grain light. After a bit of experimenting, I discovered that if I bumped the tool handle firmly down against the stop *twice* instead of only *once*, just before dropping the powder, that smaller bushing delivered the necessary half-grain extra propellant like clockwork. Such is the importance of uniform tool operation in loading shotshells!

Wadding made the difference in the load twenty years ago, and it still does. Nowadays, though, wad selection and loading have been vastly simplified by the ever-present one-piece wad which incorporates an over-powder cup, a collapsible cushioning structure, and a shot cup in a single unit. These little plastic dinguses have revolutionized shotshell loading. There must be some money to be made in plastic wads, for everybody and his kid brother in the ammunition industry seems to be rushing to get a new wad on the market. There are literally dozens of brands and

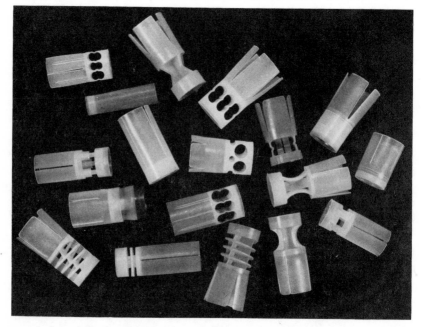

A few of the hundreds of brands, sizes, and patterns of one-piece plastic wads on the market today.

types available, all of which do the same job in only slightly different ways. They come in varying diameters, lengths, capacities, and colors, and are by no means interchangeable. However, although it may be called heresy on my part, I can find no magic in one brand over another. Select and use them according to the manufacturers' recommendations, and your shooting life will be happy and placid.

Wad-seating pressure was—and is—rather critical with multipiece, built-up wad columns, but the one-piece wads have eliminated all that. You merely seat them firmly to provide proper crimping space in the finished load, and forget it. There is one hazard in them, though, and it arises from the fact that today's plastic cases retain strong vestiges of their original crimp. If one of the points of the shell's lip happens to force its way between the fingers of the wad guide far enough to nick the skirt of the overpowder cup on the wad, that cartridge will surely deliver a blown pattern. This occurrence produces a distinct catch in the wad-seating stroke of the tool handle; be alert for it.

One-piece wads with shotcups are very convenient, but they are not necessarily the ultimate answer to all reloading problems. For one thing, they may tighten patterns more than is desirable, especially in some of the older shotguns. For another, they're relatively expensive. Smith & Wesson/Fiocchi, formerly Alcan, still offers a fair selection of multipiece wad column components in most gauges, and it's possible that we're

Although not as popular today as in the past, built-up wad column components are still sold. At left are 12-gauge fiber wads, nitro cards, and plastic over-powder cups. At right at 20-gauge cork wad, OP cups, nitro cards, and plastic shot wrappers.

about to see a renaissance of such "outdated" wad assemblies. The latest thing in factory target loads, as this is written, is special, new, multipiece wad columns. Let some name shooter win the national skeet championship with such ammo, and all those crates and cartons of wad components in my garage will be worth a fortune!

The final element inside a shotshell is the shot itself. As mentioned, most shot today is alloyed lead, usually called "black shot." The older distinctions between "chilled" and "drop" shot are no longer operative. My tests indicate that the shot sold for reloading is somewhat softer than that loaded in factory ammunition, but there's not much we can do about it. Nickel-plated shot is not, as far as I know, available on the reloading market and would be frightfully expensive if it were. Copper-plated shot is almost as good, less costly, and, best of all, available in 5-pound bags instead of the 25-pound packages in which black shot comes. On the average, substituting copper-plated pellets for plain lead in a given load, if all else remains the same, will result in approximately 10 percent denser patterns. This is a substantial improvement for long-range waterfowl and similar loadings, and well worth the extra cost for the relatively few rounds a hunter will load in a season. It is also one kind of component substitution which is perfectly acceptable.

One which isn't involves the so-called iron shot about which such a furor has arisen in waterfowl hunting in recent years. Actually a form of

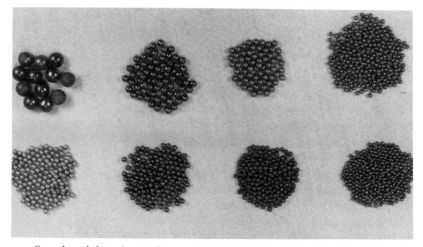

Samples of shot sizes and types available for handloading include (top row, from left) #9, #7½, #6 lead, #6 copper-plated, (bottom row) #8, #4, #2, and 0 buckshot.

mild steel, the pellets are nontoxic to waterfowl which ingest them while feeding. Steel shot has a lower specific gravity than lead, and thus a lower sectional density, which means that it is ballistically inferior to lead. Much larger pellets of steel are required to give the same penetration as smaller lead ones, and effective ranges are reduced to a maximum of about 40 yards by steel shot. Some guns may be damaged by its use, too, but there's every indication that environmental extremists may force the use of steel shot for duck and goose hunting throughout the nation within a season or two.

If so, you have no alternative but to quit waterfowling or purchase factory-loaded ammunition with steel shot. Steel shot requires powders, wads, and techniques not now available to handloaders. It cannot be safely and effectively reloaded with *any* components presently available to us. *Don't* try it, even if you happen to come by a supply of the shot by some mysterious chance. Furthermore, don't attempt to use anything like ball bearings as a substitute. You'll only ruin your gun. There appears to be some hope that other, even more exotic forms of shot pellets may be developed in time to avoid the use of steel. The most-talked-about experiment at the moment is sintered shot, of varying proportions of iron and lead, which is said to be nontoxic to waterfowl while retaining acceptable ballistic properties. Perhaps we'll all be stuffing shotshells with such stuff in the near future, but, for now, a safe rule is: *use lead shot and nothing else* for reloading shotgun ammunition.

Few gunners fire buckshot or slug ammo in sufficient quantity to justify the rather tedious process of handloading it. Even if they do, equaling the performance of factory ammunition is very unlikely in slug loads and next to impossible with buckshot. Nevertheless, it's perfectly possible to produce reasonably efficient loads of either type at home. Ready-to-load 12-gauge slugs with wadding attached are sold by Brenneke and Vitt, or you can cast your own from pure lead in a Lyman mold. The latter is available in 20- and 16-gauge, as well. Case mouths in slug loads are closed with a roll crimp rather than the standard folded crimp, and Lyman sells a roll-crimping head to be used in a drill press for this purpose. The manufacturers furnish load data, which should be followed with considerable care.

The secret to the remarkable success of factory-loaded buckshot seems to be in the use of a granulated plastic filler around and between the individual pellets, plus a plastic wrapper. Handloaders have attempted to duplicate such loads using flour, cornmeal, and probably powdered horse manure, with indifferent success. I believe that Herter's still sells a granulated polyethylene for just such use, and it seems to be the current best bet for reloaders. However, the mechanical problems of getting the stuff evenly distributed among the pellets and making it stay there are diverse, and I am unaware of any technique discovered so far which consistently duplicates the performance of the factory items.

The plastic wrapper is available from S&W/Fiocchi as the Alcan "Kwik-Sert," and the same firm can sell you the special, multipiece wad-column elements needed for buckshot loads (one-piece wad units are unsuitable).

On the whole, the best reasons I can think of for loading your own buckshot or slug ammo are (1) to say you've done it, and (2) so that you'll fully appreciate the cartridges inside those neat little five-packs of buck or slug loads when you pick one up from your sporting goods dealer.

27
Shotshell Tools

The first decision a reloader must make before purchasing a shot-shell-loading tool concerns his production-volume requirements. Will he be happy loading hulls at the rate of perhaps one box (25) in an hour's time, or does he need to produce as many as 600 within the same period? The Lee Loader will satisfy the first need, and there are tools available from Ponsness, Pacific, and MEC which meet or even exceed the second specification. The Lee Loader sells as of this writing for less than $10 complete, and the big Ponsness-Warren Model 800-B can be yours for only $500, the tenth part of a $5,000 bill. The Ponsness-Warren loads shells so rapidly that maximum production can be achieved only with a two-man crew, one to operate the machine and the other to keep components moving and hoppers filled.

Between these extremes lie most of the shotshell loading tools on the market today. Production rates average between 100 and about 250 rounds per hour, and prices range between $60 and about $100. Such equipment is offered by Bair, Pacific, Redding, Texan, MEC, Lyman, Herter's, and Ponsness. These so-called single-storage tools normally require at least one hand motion (other than operating the handle) per operation. The operations are decapping the spent hull, seating a fresh primer, dropping the powder charge, seating the wad or wads, dropping

This Redding shotshell tool is solidly built and durable.

the shot charge, crimp-starting, and final crimping, in that order. The shell will probably be resized somewhere among those steps. In some systems, the case is driven into a resizing die and remains in it as it is moved from station to station, in order to prevent wad-seating and crimping forces from swelling the hull enough to cause chambering trouble in an autoloading gun. In others, resizing occurs at the decapping station, and in still other systems it's integral with the crimping operation.

All shotshell tools have powder and shot hoppers built in. Some have automatic primer feeds, either integral or as an optional accessory. On the high-production presses, all the operator has to do is insert empty hulls at one end, position wads for seating, pull the lever, and take loaded rounds from the other end. He gets a fully loaded cartridge with each pull of the

The Texan FW shotshell tool is a top-of-the-line loader, with a capacity of at least 100 rounds per hour in the hands of an experienced operator.

handle. The Hydramec Super 600 even eliminates all that tiresome handle-yanking; it's operated by an electrically controlled hydraulic system so that the reloader has only to touch a foot pedal for each cycle.

In general, the higher the production rate of which a tool is capable, the less flexible it is, especially for loading small batches of shells for experimental shooting. Therefore, the gunner who intends to load only one type of ammunition and who fires great quantities of that ammo (and who can afford one) is best served by one of the big, mass-production tools. On the other hand, the hunter who likes to play around with loads to optimize the performance of his guns and who may wish to assemble some target loads, some for pheasants, a few for ducks and geese, and maybe some turkey or even buckshot cartridges is better off with one of the simpler tools. He will find it much easier to adjust when changing loads, and it should still easily produce at least 100 rounds of ammo per hour, enough for most shooters. There is a tendency on the part of new shotshell loaders to buy too much tool.

All the reloading tools with which I am familiar on the market today will reload good ammunition, usable in any kind of gun, provided they're adjusted and operated competently. Actually shooting in the gun in question is, of course, the acid test, but shotshell reloads can be judged quite accurately on the appearance of their crimps. The crimp should be neatly folded and perfectly flat, with the rolled lips smooth and never larger in diameter than the body of the hull itself. Today's plastic factory ammo has heat-sealed crimps (except Federal's) and a small portion at the very center of the crimp shoots away when the shell is fired. This will leave a very small hole at the center of the crimp closure when that case is reloaded. It's normal and, as long as it isn't large enough to allow a shot pellet to escape, it's not a flaw. Also, inspect the case body just ahead of the brass head; if there's a wrinkle or roll there, some adjustments are necessary for that type of case in that machine. However, demonstration reloaders set up in a sporting-goods shop are usually properly adjusted, and the finished appearance of the crimp is your best mark. The more the reload crimp resembles a factory load's, the better.

By the way, hulls are available today which were closed when loaded at a factory with either a six- or an eight-fold crimp. Plastic shells insist on having subsequent crimps folded along exactly the same lines, which means that you'll save yourself trouble in the long run if you purchase both a six-point and an eight-point crimp-starter when you buy the tool.

Powder and shot charges are controlled in all tools by means of cavities which meter the materials by volume. In some tools, these are in fixed bars, so that to change loads one must switch bars (some charge bars have interchangeable bushings for the shot), while in other systems the size of both powder and shot cavities is controlled by replaceable bushings. Bars with micrometer-adjustable cavities for both propellant and pellets are also available. As the handloader accumulates more different bushings or bars, a potential hazard grows, and it is that he will inadvertently install the wrong bushings for the load he intends to assemble. A larger powder bushing can drop a dangerous overload, and a larger shot bushing can, even in conjunction with the correct powder bushing, elevate pressures by dumping too great a weight of pellets. Sometimes, one of these mistakes will create a components column in the hull over which it cannot be crimped, but all too often a little extra force on the operating handle will crimp the load. Perhaps "bomb" would be a better term than "load." A similar result can be obtained in some tool designs by care-

The crimp produced by a shotshell loader when properly adjusted is a good criterion of the quality of the equipment and of the cartridges which can be produced with it. Here are satisfactory crimps in shells of variety of types and gauges, showing both 6- and 8-point crimps, plastic and paper (extreme right) hulls, field and target loads. The handload second from left has been sealed with a drop of hot wax to improve moisture resistance for waterfowling.

lessly filling the powder hopper with shot and the shot hopper with powder and reversing the sequence of operation of the charge bar. Normally, powder and shot bushings have different outside diameters, so that they can't be inadvertently exchanged in the bar itself. Always make certain you have the correct bushing installed, the correct powder in the hopper, and powder and shot in the correct hoppers.

Loading dies are available in .410, 28-, 20-, 16-, 12-, and 10-gauge, and die sets can be interchanged on almost all shotshell presses. Extra die sets, however, cost from about $25 to almost $50, depending upon maker, and changing over from one gauge to another usually entails at least an hour or so of exasperating work and ruined hulls while making final adjustments. The Ponsness-Warren Du-O-Matic press can be set up permanently with dies for two different gauges in its turret, making changeover a five-minute job. Most reloaders who wish to load for more than one gauge, however, eventually get around to the concept of having a different press for each gauge, with dies permanently installed, adjusted, and locked. Rumblings from the industry as this is written suggest that more manufacturers are working on the idea of quick-change die sets, and I suspect this will be the next major change in shotshell presses.

Most systems permit the switch from standard (2¾-inch) to magnum (3-inch) cases within a given gauge by changing only one or two dies in the tool and readjusting the others.

The shotshell loader needs fewer accessory tools than the metallics man. A powder scale is necessary to verify powder and shot bushings, and, for the latter, a large-capacity scale is desirable, preferably weighing to at least 1,000 grains. For loaders who enjoy playing with different loads, an

Powder and shot bushings are made of steel, aluminum, or brass, depending upon the maker. At top is an adjustable charge bar for the MEC shotshell loaders.

adjustable powder measure like those used by metallics handloaders is very handy, since no man alive ever had every single powder bushing he needed for any conceivable load.

Shell conditioners are sold by Lyman, RCBS, MEC, Forster, and others. Some of these resize cases, heads, and rims (diameter and thickness), flatten heads, clean and iron mouths, and even deprime. Others have integral or optional heating elements to melt the wax and iron out paper hulls. There's no doubt that running your precious cases through this extra step before reloading will lengthen their loading lives and provide neater, firmer reloads, but such equipment is not mandatory for shotshell loading.

Most of the remaining gadgets marketed for shotshell stuffing are highly specialized. If you need it, you'll be aware of its presence on the market. They include shotshell trimmers, special wad guides, rollcrimping devices, and so forth. Most handloaders get along nicely with only a loading tool and a scale.

Familiarity with your tool is one of the keys to good reloads for shotguns. There is a certain rhythm to loading shotshells which one develops with experience, and any variation from the normal "feel" of the equipment in operation serves as a warning signal. Uniformity in operating technique is just as important to consistent shotshell reloads as it is in operating a powder measure. Every movement should be performed exactly the same every time, with the same force and the same rhythm. Whenever a catch is noticed or greater or lesser force than expected is required, stop and sort out the causes. It may be that a point on the case mouth

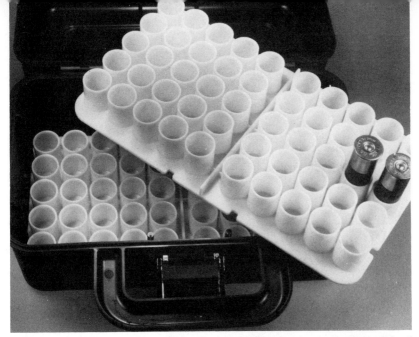

MTM offers this handy shotshell carrying case which can hold 100 rounds of any gauge (or 50 each of two different gauges). The plastic trays are especially handy to the reloader as loading blocks.

pushed between the fingers of the wad guide to catch and nick the wad skirt, or that a case or a wad different from those being loaded got mixed into the supply, unnoticed. It's easy to load excellent shotshells with the equipment now available, but it isn't automatic. The operator must still give his entire attention to the process at all times.

Shotshell stuffing is the classic example of an activity in which it pays to make haste slowly. Most of us are striving for maximum production rates, but not at the cost of inferior ammo. Slap-dash, slam-bang operation of a shotshell tool is the wrong way to hurry. Steady, smooth, unhurried operation produces better ammo faster in the long run, and wastes fewer components in the process.

I will never forget my feelings one afternoon on a skeet range when about half of my 20-gauge reloads actually failed to fire. I (gun expert, reloading author, etc.) got some looks ranging from politely quizzical to outright sneers as I lost bird after bird when the gun went click instead of bang. When I got home, I did what I should have done and hadn't in my haste, the day before when I'd loaded the ammunition. I inspected the fired cases from which I'd drawn those which had failed. Sure enough, about half of them had one or more mourning-dove feathers inside, from having been dropped into my game bag with the doves on my last hunting excursion. I hadn't bothered to take the time to really check the cases before loading, and as a result my ego and local reputation had suffered in the process.

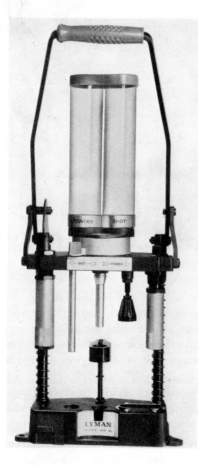

This straight-line shotshell load-ing press is one of the fastest available.

I was lucky, at that. A little embarrassment is a minor penalty to pay for unwarranted haste in reloading. Even blown patterns are substantially better than blown shotguns, and that can happen, too, when a hand-loader begins to measure his success solely in terms of boxes per hour.

28

A Round-Up
of Reloading Safety

Throughout this book I have attempted to note essential safety considerations relative to every reloading operation. Even so, perhaps it's worth while to condense in this last chapter a review of the general safety principles for easy reference. Almost fifteen years ago, I wrote a humorous article on reloading safety for a firearms magazine. Since then, I have noted that most of the ideas I set forth in that article have appeared on various lists of safety rules for handloaders, although I do not remember having seen such a list before that writing. This, of course, is not to be taken as a claim that I invented the rules. They are nothing more than plain old common sense, bolstered by experience. In fact, the first rule on the list is just that:

Exercise care and common sense at all times while reloading. Another way to put it would be: THINK! Think of what you're doing, and think of the possible consequences of your actions at each step of the process.

The second general rule is really a restatement of this one: *Pay attention to the business at hand while at the loading bench.* Don't try to load while watching a TV football game out of the corner of your eye. Don't invite a bunch of your buddies over and attempt to carry your end of a general bull session while stuffing ammo. Reloading is fairly technical

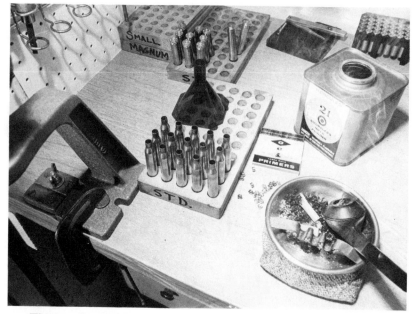

This is a photograph of an accident waiting to happen: Loose primers, open powder cans, and burning tobacco do *not* mix, a rule so obvious it shouldn't require repeating.

activity and mistakes can be serious. Don't permit distractions in the same room with your loading tools.

I said it in the last chapter about shotshells, but *Never reload in haste* applies just as fully to every other aspect of handloading. Loading in a hurry can mean an unnoticed wrong setting on a powder scale or even the wrong powder in the measure. At best, haste defeats the whole purpose of reloading, which is superior ammunition for your guns. At worst, it's disaster.

Use equipment as the manufacturer intended, and do not take shortcuts. Self-explanatory; jerry-rigging is usually bad news.

Store powder in a cool dry place. Along with this one should do the following: Store powder in small quantities, in approved containers, away from such combustibles as solvents, inflammable gases, and, of course, open flame. Furthermore, keep gunpowder away from children and vice versa.

Never use a powder unless you're positive of its identity. Repeat: *never!* Don't guess, and don't try to identify gunpowder by its physical appearance. Not even an expert can do it. The one and only acceptable identification of a powder is the label on its can, provided it is still in the factory container in which it was originally packaged.

Never smoke while handling powder. Surely this is too obvious to need comment, especially to anyone intelligent enough to read this book.

Never mix gunpowders. Not in a cartridge case and not in a canister. If the latter happens as a result of violations of other safety rules, destroy the resultant mixture. Do *not* attempt to extrapolate a new burning rate for the mix and use it; relative quickness is not all that simple.

Never store small-arms primers in any kind of container except the factory packaging. Period, end of paragraph.

Observe all maximum load warnings in reloading manuals. See my discussion of this in the chapter on powder charging and load development. A corollary is: *Approach those maximums only from 10 percent below.*

Inspect all cases—rifle, pistol, or shotgun—for condition before loading, and discard any which are less than perfect. Trying to squeeze just one more shot out of weakened brass has spelled catastrophe for more than one reloader. It ain't worth it.

Watch for signs of high pressure while working up a handload. This means extraction difficulty (however slight), flattened primers, cratered primers, ironed-out headstamps, polished headstamps, ejector marks, case-head expansion, and excessive recoil and muzzle blast. And anything else whatever which strikes you as abnormal about the load.

Develop a routine in reloading to guard against mistakes, just in case your attention does occasionally wander. You'll form habits at the loading bench anyway; it's just as easy to establish well-thought-out habits for safety as slipshod ones which may permit you to slip into dangerous practices without realizing it. This rule really applies as much to shooting your handloads as to making them up. For example, a personal rule of having never more than one ammunition box open on the shooting bench at one time may prevent your trying to fire the wrong cartridge in a rifle.

Safety in handloading goes, of course, farther than just common sense, even though most of us are sensible enough to figure out what we should and should not be doing. Still, sometimes it's helpful to tune into the suggestions of those who serve as watchdogs of handloading, the Sporting Arms and Ammunition Manufacturers' Institute, or SAAMI. They have compiled the following list of do's and don'ts for the handloader. Some of their rules more or less repeat some I have just given, but information of this sort can certainly bear repeating. After all, we're talking about avoiding some potentially serious accidents.

SAAMI DO'S AND DON'T'S FOR HANDLOADERS

GENERAL

Follow *only* loading recommendations of a recognized current handloading guide. Better still, check 2 guides. Components and propellants change and old recommendations may be dangerous.

Don't use word of mouth loading data without checking a recognized current handloading guide.

Have the headspace of your firearm checked by a competent gunsmith at regular intervals, preferably by a factory authorized repair station.

Examine fired cases for signs of excessive pressure such as primer gas leaks, excessive primer flattening, loose primers, expanded heads or bodies, side wall stretching.

Investigate and determine the cause of any unusual or abnormal condition or appearance before continuing any operation.

Keep all components and loaded rounds positively identified.

Keep your work area and handloading bench scrupulously clean at all times. Immediately clean up any spillage of powder, primers, etc.

Do not chamber a round that resists easy closing of the bolt or action. The cartridge is too long or large in diameter and high pressure may develop.

Do not forget that a maximum load in your rifle may be dangerous in another one of your rifles or in a friend's rifle even if it is the same make, model, caliber, etc.

Components suitable for lead shot loads are *not* adaptable to steel shot loads.

The interchange of steel shot for lead results in dangerously high pressures which may damage shotguns. Ball bearings or steel air rifle shot are not suitable for shotshell loads. They are greatly harder than steel shot.

Keep all components out of the reach of children.

Keep accurate detailed records of all loads.

Do not load with charges that measure out to more than 10% below minimum recommendations.

Cartridge cases should be clean and dry before reloading and before firing. Oily cases greatly increase thrust against the bolt face.

Do not fire form factory cartridges in lengthened chambers. The excessive headspace is likely to be dangerous.

Be extremely careful to identify properly wildcat cases since the headstamp does not represent the new cartridge which may have a larger diameter bullet than the original cartridge.

Do not use too much heat to dry cases to avoid softening the brass.

Do not use brass cases that have been in or near a fire.

COMPONENTS

Bullets • Be sure that they are the recommended diameter and weight. Keep bullet calibers and weights in separate and accurately marked containers.

Do not mix or interchange bullets from various manufacturers in the same reloading formula.

Don't substitute calibers, use only that which your gun is chambered for exactly, e.g. 300 Winchester Magnum is not a 300 Savage.

Primers • Inspect for presence of anvils before seating. Store only in original manufacturers' package. Keep a minimum amount on your loading bench. Remove unused primers from your loading tool after each session and return to the original package for storage.

Keep out of reach of children.

Store in a cool dry place.

Do not store primers in bulk. Mass detonation may occur. Use only the brand of primers specified in the loading recommendations.

Cases • Do not mix brands—case volume may be different affecting loading density and pressure. Inspect for cracks, splits, stretch marks separations, etc. after firing and before reloading. Do not load damaged or defective cases. Do not ream or enlarge primer flash holes.

Examine fired shot shells for head damage, tube splits, pin holes, location of base wad before reloading. Discard defective cases. Discard cases which show leakage around the primer or battery cup.

Do not mix shells with high and low base wads.

Do not mix brands of cases—volumes may be different.

Powder • Store in a cool, dry place in the original container in an approved storage cabinet. Keep container closed except when pouring.

Keep powder out of reach of children.

Have only one type and speed on your bench at one time to avoid mixing types.

Keep a minimum amount of powder in the loading area.

Never mix powders.

Don't use any powder that you are not sure of its identity. Do not use any powder that appears discolored or is giving off fumes.

Wads • Use only the specific type listed in the recommendations.

Do not mix or interchange types as pressure levels can be affected.

Don't mix powders of the same type designation made by different companies. DuPont IMR 4350 is not the same as Hodgdon's H 4350.

Shot • Check weight of charge thrown by your measure or bar to be sure it conforms to the recommendations.

LOADING OPERATIONS

Avoid distractions while performing any of the loading operations.
Keep all matches and smoking materials out of the loading area.
Do not smoke in the loading area because of the possibility of primer residue or powder which might become ignited.

Decapping • Use proper decapping pin to avoid distorting or enlarging the flash hole. Examine flash holes for roundness, burrs and enlargement before repriming. Do not remove live primers by driving out of the case with a sharp hammer blow. Decap in a press slowly.

Resizing • Lubricate sparingly to avoid oil dents in the shoulder area of the case. Some lubricant must be used to prevent scratches from dirt on the cases and in the dies.
Check overall case length and trim the mouth when case elongates beyond recommended length. Check neck wall thickness and ream or turn to original thickness to assure adequate clearance between case neck and chamber.
Be sure that the resizing die is properly adjusted so that the shoulder of the case is not set back too far producing excessive clearance between the shoulder of the case and the chamber.

Priming • Inspect pockets and clean before inserting new primers.
Seat primers slowly with a punch that conforms to the profile of the primer to flush or slightly below the case head. Do not prime cases with a hammer or mallet. It is a dangerous practice. The object is to seat the legs of the primer anvil on the bottom of the primer pocket. Case should be held by the rim or on a vented punch in the event that a primer may fire. Discard cases in which the primer is loose in the pocket.
After each loading session wipe base of the tool with a slightly oily rag to pick up any primer mixture dust.
Do not use pistol primers for rifle cartridges or rifle primers in pistol or revolver cartridges. The thicker primer cup of rifle primers may cause misfires in pistols while the thinner cup of pistol primers may pierce or blank at the higher pressure levels of rifle cartridges.
Do not use pistol or revolver or rifle primers in shotshells. The priming charge is inadequate for proper ignition of the powder. A transparent shield of lucite or equivalent is recommended between the loading machine and the operator.
Use only a well-designed and constructed tool.
Seating of primers with a hammer and punch is dangerous.

Powder Charging • Inspect the inside of all cases for foreign objects before dropping a charge into the case.

If a powder measure is used, the first five charges thrown by the measure should be weighed on a reliable scale and checked against the recommendations. Periodic checks for weight should be made to be sure that uniform weights are being thrown.

Examine charged cases to be sure that no gross errors in charging have been made, i.e. double charges or empties. A simple powder height gauge is recommended.

Start with the minimum charge recommended and watch for pressure signs on the fired cases from your firearm before increasing.

Do not load more than one charge per case.

Bullet Seating • Seat bullets to the length recommendations only. Pressures are affected by cartridges that are either too long or too short.

If cartridges are to be used in either box or tubular magazines, a mouth crimp is recommended to prevent lengthening or shortening due to recoil.

Be sure bullets are tight in the neck to be sure that the bullet will not pull out if a loaded round is extracted.

Do not load by changing bullets in loaded rounds even if the weights are the same.

After loading shotshells, the crimps should be inspected for uniform depth. Excessive length variation may indicate a loading error which could be dangerous.

Do not seal the crimp with tape.

Reloading centerfire ammunition ranks far below children's toys as a source of accidental injury. Overall, it's a remarkably safe pastime, especially considering the volatile nature of some of the components being handled. The potential for accidents is inherent in the man and not in the hobby, equipment, or materials. By the same token, *you* are your own margin of safety—and mine, if I happen to be shooting on the next bench at the rifle range. And, since I happen to value both readers and my scalp very dearly, I trust you'll heed these safety rules.

See you at the range.

Index